REVISE EDEXCEL GCSE (9—
Geography A

D0524435

REVISION GUIDE

Series Consultant: Harry Smith

Author: Michael Chiles

A note from the publisher

In order to ensure that this resource offers high-quality support for the associated Pearson qualification, it has been through a review process by the awarding body. This process confirms that this resource fully covers the teaching and learning content of the specification or part of a specification at which it is aimed. It also confirms that it demonstrates an appropriate balance between the development of subject skills, knowledge and understanding, in addition to preparation for assessment.

Endorsement does not cover any guidance on assessment activities or processes (e.g. practice questions or advice on how to answer assessment questions), included in the resource nor does it prescribe any particular approach to the teaching or delivery of a related course.

While the publishers have made every attempt to ensure that advice on the qualification and its assessment

is accurate, the official specification and associated assessment guidance materials are the only authoritative source of information and should always be referred to for definitive guidance.

Pearson examiners have not contributed to any sections in this resource relevant to examination papers for which they have responsibility.

Examiners will not use endorsed resources as a source of material for any assessment set by Pearson.

Endorsement of a resource does not mean that the resource is required to achieve this Pearson qualification, nor does it mean that it is the only suitable material available to support the qualification, and any resource lists produced by the awarding body shall include this and other appropriate resources.

Contents

Edexcel publishes Sample Assessment Material and the Specification on its website. This is the official content and this book should be used in conjunction with it. The questions in Now try this have been written to help you practise every topic in the book. Remember: the real exam questions may not look like this.

Main UK rock types

The UK is made up of many rock types, but the three main groups are sedimentary, igneous and metamorphic.

Main UK rock types

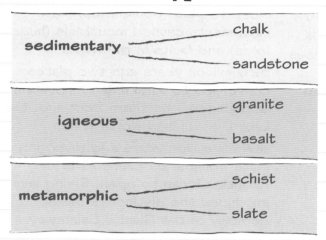

sedimentary — chalk / sandstone

igneous — granite / basalt

metamorphic — schist / slate

Distribution of UK rock types

- ☐ sedimentary
- ☐ igneous
- ☐ metamorphic

Edinburgh, Belfast, Dublin, Nottingham, Cardiff, London

Sedimentary rocks

Sedimentary rocks are formed in layers called beds. They often contain fossils. Examples include chalk and sandstone.

- ✓ **Chalk** is made up of calcium carbonate, and is susceptible to chemical weathering.
- ✓ **Sandstone** is made of sand-sized grains cemented together. It can be hard and resistant to weathering, but is permeable.

Igneous rocks

Igneous rocks are hard and formed of crystals so are resistant to erosion. They are usually impermeable – water doesn't pass through them. Examples include granite and basalt.

- ✓ **Granite** is affected by chemical weathering. Granite landscapes drain badly, so tend to be boggy.
- ✓ **Basalt** is a grey rock made from very small crystals. Lava flows cool to form basalt.

Worked example

Study the photograph, which shows slate, a metamorphic rock. Explain how metamorphic rocks form. **(2 marks)**

Metamorphic rocks are formed by great heat and pressure. Examples are schist and slate. Slate is formed from mudstone at convergent plate boundaries. Schist is formed at higher pressure at the same plate boundary.

Slate splits easily into thin layers

When you are asked to explain **how**, remember to include the key points of the process.

Now try this

Explain **two** differences between igneous and sedimentary rocks. **(2 marks)**

Upland and lowland landscapes

Geology and **past** tectonic activity have influenced the physical landscapes of the UK.

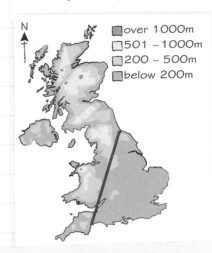

The imaginary Tees–Exe line divides the UK into uplands (north) and lowlands (south).

Map key:
- over 1000m
- 501 – 1000m
- 200 – 500m
- below 200m

Geology

The UK is split into two halves geologically.

- The north-western UK is mainly harder igneous and metamorphic rocks, forming **upland** landscapes.
- The south-eastern UK is mainly softer sedimentary rocks, forming **lowland** landscapes.

Plate tectonics

Millions of years ago the UK was close to plate boundaries. Plate movements caused mountains (huge folds) and faults in the rocks.

520 million years ago two plates converged to form upland mountain landscapes – northern Scotland, the Lake District and North Wales.

50–60 million years ago diverging plate boundaries caused the Atlantic Ocean to open. Rising lava produced the distinctive basalt geology of the Giant's Causeway.

Distinct landscapes

North-west of the Tees–Exe line the UK's geology is largely igneous: rocks formed from magma and lava, associated with tectonic events. Long-extinct volcanoes form hills and mountains.

Basalt can form a very distinct landscape as the lava cools into polygon shapes: for example, the Giant's Causeway in Northern Ireland and Fingal's Cave in Scotland.

Worked example

Study the geological cross-section, showing the rocks forming part of south-east England.

a Name the rock group to which these rocks belong. **(1 mark)**

Sedimentary

b Explain why lowland landscapes are usually formed by this rock group. **(2 marks)**

Sedimentary rocks are much softer and more easily eroded than igneous and metamorphic rocks. Therefore sedimentary rocks are worn down rapidly to form low hills and lowland basins.

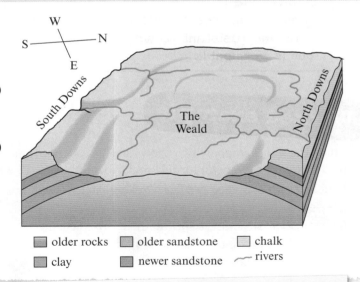

Key:
- older rocks
- clay
- older sandstone
- newer sandstone
- chalk
- rivers

The distance between the North and South Downs is about 60 km so the geological cross-section shows a large area.

Now try this

Study the map of the UK rock types on page 1. Explain **one** reason why upland Britain is made up of igneous and metamorphic rocks.

(2 marks)

Physical processes

Some distinctive upland and lowland UK landscapes result from physical processes working together: glacial erosion and deposition, weathering and climatological processes, and post-glacial river and slope processes.

Ordnance Survey Maps, © Crown copyright 2016, OS 100030901 and supplied by courtesy of Maps International

This upland landscape is in the Lake District. The OS map extract scale is 1:25000.

- **Glacial erosion:** Stickle Tarn, in the north, is where a glacier formed during the Ice Age and carved out a corrie.
  See page 26 for more on glacial erosion.

- **Weathering:** the crags are exposed rock faces. Weathering leads to rock fragments breaking off and falling to the base of the cliff to form a scree slope.
  See page 25 for more on freeze–thaw weathering.

- **Climate:** high precipitation here means there is a lot of surface drainage over the impermeable rocks; there are many streams.

- **Post-glacial river:** the valley floor at the bottom is too wide for the stream to have eroded it. The flat bottom and steep sides shows that it is a U-shaped valley formed by a glacier.

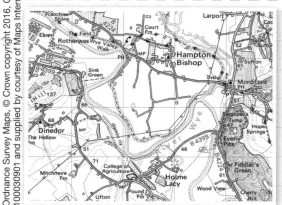

Ordnance Survey Maps, © Crown copyright 2016, OS 100030901 and supplied by courtesy of Maps International

This lowland landscape is in Herefordshire. The OS map extract scale is 1:50000. The landscape has been formed by the actions of two rivers: the River Lugg and the River Wye.

- **River erosion:** as the rivers meander, they have eroded a wide valley between low hills. The rivers transport silt eroded from the river channel.
  See page 15 for more on transport and deposition.

- **River deposition:** prolonged heavy rain can cause the rivers to flood. Water spreads out all over the valley floor, depositing the silt to form a wide, flat floodplain.
  See page 19 for more on floodplain formation.

Worked example

Study the photograph of Bowerman's Nose, Dartmoor, a tor made of granite. Explain how it has formed from the interaction of physical processes. **(4 marks)**

Dartmoor formed when a dome of magma (batholith) developed underground 290 million years ago. The magma cooled and contracted to form granite, with cooling joints. Chemical weathering caused the joints to widen. Granite was exposed on the surface. Freeze–thaw weathering, erosion and mass movement removed the broken granite. Outcrops of rock less affected by weathering and erosion are left behind, forming tors.

This answer clearly explains how several processes working together formed granite landscapes.

Now try this

Which of the following rocks is **not** formed of crystals? **(1 mark)**

☐ **A** Granite ☐ **B** Chalk ☐ **C** Schist ☐ **D** Basalt

Human activity

The UK has been settled by humans for many thousands of years and all its landscapes have been heavily influenced by human activity.

Ordnance Survey Maps, © Crown copyright 2016, OS 100030901 and supplied by courtesy of Maps International

Agriculture

This OS map extract is at 1:25 000 scale.
It shows a region of Suffolk in the east of the UK.

- The blue lines are drainage ditches, built to drain water away from low-lying agricultural land to allow crops to grow.
- Straight drainage ditches are not produced by natural physical processes so they are a good indication of human activity.

Humans have altered almost all the landscapes of the UK through farming. Different farming types are suited to different landscapes: for example, sheep farming in upland areas and arable farming in fertile lowland valleys.

Forestry

Forestry is managing woodland for timber.

- Many UK upland landscapes have been planted with trees for forestry. Sometimes they are in straight rows to make them easy to manage.
- The UK would naturally be covered by deciduous woodland. However, some UK landscapes feature conifer plantations, which are very distinctive.

When trees are felled for timber, a section of the plantation may be cleared. This aerial photo shows a cleared area in the Strathyre Forest, Scotland.

Worked example

Explain why lowland landscapes have been more altered by human settlement than upland landscapes. **(4 marks)**

Settlements grew up where the landscape offered advantages, such as flat land that is easier to build on. Lowland landscapes also provided river meander loops where it was easy to defend towns, coastal plains and natural harbours for fishing villages and shallow points on rivers where fords could be made (for example, Oxford). Over time, the settlements spread over the landscape. In big cities, many streams and small rivers now run in underground tunnels, so cannot be seen on maps. Upland landscapes of hills and mountains make it more difficult to construct settlements so are less built up.

The question asks about **both** lowland **and** upland landscapes – make sure you include both in your answer.

Now try this

The map below shows the Shropshire town of Shrewsbury. Suggest **one** reason why the site of Shrewsbury was chosen for a settlement. **(2 marks)**

Ordnance Survey Maps, © Crown copyright 2016, OS 100030901 and supplied by courtesy of Maps International

Physical processes 1

The coastline is shaped by the interaction of the different physical processes of weathering, mass movement and erosion. You need to understand how each process causes change along coastlines.

Weathering on the coast

Weathering helps wear away rocks but leaves weathered material **in situ**. There are three types of weathering.

Chemical – rocks reacting with slightly acidic water, e.g. limestone dissolved by **carbonation**

Biological – action of plants and animals (e.g. tree roots widen in cracks in rocks), causing the rock to split apart

Weathering

Mechanical – water falls into the cracks in rocks and freezes, causing it to expand; over time the repeated thawing and freezing causes the rock to break apart

> In this component you must study **two** of Coastal, River and Glaciated landscapes. Only revise this section if it is one of the two you have studied.

Mass movement on the coast

Mass movement is the downhill movement of material under the influence of gravity. Types of mass movement vary according to:

- material involved
- amount of water in the material
- type of movement, e.g. sliding, slumping.

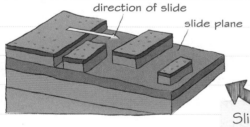

direction of slide
slide plane

> Sliding happens when loosened rocks and soil suddenly slide down the slope. Blocks of material may all slide at once.

How waves erode the coast

Abrasion: breaking waves throw sand, pebbles and boulders against the coast during storms.

Hydraulic action: the sheer weight and impact of water against the coastline, particularly during a storm, erodes the coast. Also waves compress air in joints in rocks, forcing them apart.

Attrition: rocks and pebbles carried by waves rub together and break into smaller pieces.

Solution: the chemical action of seawater dissolves some rocks.

Worked example

Study the diagram opposite. Explain how slumping occurs.

(2 marks)

Slumping happens when the rock is saturated. Loose, wet rocks slump down under the pull of gravity along curved slip planes.

> Slumping often happens on clay coasts.

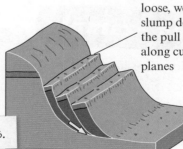

loose, wet rocks slump down under the pull of gravity along curved slip planes

Now try this

Explain how sliding can cause downhill movement of material. **(3 marks)**

 Remember to read questions like this carefully, and don't mix up sliding and slumping.

5

Physical processes 2

Waves transport eroded material along the coast and deposit it when they lose the energy to carry it further.

In this component you must study **two** of Coastal, River and Glaciated landscapes. **Only revise this section if it is one of the two you have studied.**

Longshore drift

This is the process by which beach sediment can be **transported** along the coast by waves.

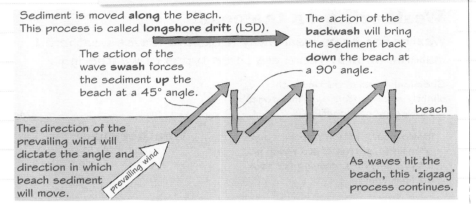

Sediment is moved **along** the beach. This process is called **longshore drift** (LSD).

The action of the wave **swash** forces the sediment **up** the beach at a 45° angle.

The action of the **backwash** will bring the sediment back **down** the beach at a 90° angle.

beach

The direction of the prevailing wind will dictate the angle and direction in which beach sediment will move.

prevailing wind

As waves hit the beach, this 'zigzag' process continues.

Transport

Waves **transport** material by:

 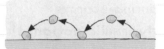

Traction – large boulders are rolled along the seabed by waves

Saltation – smaller stones are bounced along the seabed

Suspension – sand and small particles are carried along in the flow

Solution – some minerals are dissolved in seawater and carried along in the flow

Deposition

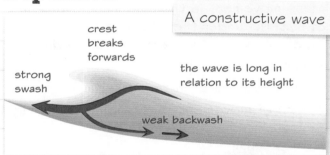

A constructive wave

crest breaks forwards

strong swash

the wave is long in relation to its height

weak backwash

The load carried by waves is deposited by constructive waves. Different factors influence deposition, for example:

• sheltered spots (e.g. bays)
• calm conditions
• gentle gradient offshore causing friction.

All reduce the wave's energy.

Worked example

The command word here is **explain**, so you need to say **how** the process happens.

Explain how longshore drift transports material along the coastline. **(4 marks)**

The direction of material movement is determined by the prevailing wind direction. Waves approach the coastline at an acute angle, bringing sediment onto the beach in the swash. Sediment is then dragged back to sea in the backwash, under the force of gravity at a right angle. This process continues in a zigzag pattern, moving sediment along the beach.

Now try this

Remember to name at least two processes here and explain how material is transported.

Explain how waves can transport material.   **(4 marks)**

Influence of geology

The geological structure of coasts, rock type and wave action all influence coastal landforms.

Only revise this section if you studied Coastal landscapes.

Geological structure

Geology affects how fast coastal erosion occurs. Soft rock is eroded much faster than hard rock. Particular landforms are created when soft rocks and hard rocks occur together.

Soft rock, such as clay

- ✓ Soft rock is easily eroded by the sea.
- ✓ Cliffs will be less rugged and less steep than hard rock coasts.
- ✓ Soft rock landscapes include bays.

Hard rock, such as granite

- ✓ Hard rock is resistant to all types of erosion.
- ✓ Cliffs will be high, steep and rugged.
- ✓ Hard rock landscapes include wave-cut platforms and headlands where caves, arches and stacks are formed.

Read more about erosional landforms on page 9.

Concordant and discordant coasts

Concordant coasts are made up of the same rock type. On discordant coasts, the rock type alternates, forming headlands and bays.

Revise these on page 9.

soft rock
hard rock
soft rock
hard rock
concordant coast
discordant coast

These two maps show the same coastline. The hard rocks are chalk and limestone; the soft rocks are mudstone, sands and clays.

Joints and faults

- Joints are smaller cracks; faults are larger.
- Both make rock more prone to erosion.
- Rocks with more joints and faults are eroded more quickly.

Worked example

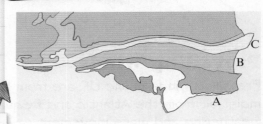

Study the geological map above. State which point marks the location of a chalk headland and stacks.

(1 mark)

C

Destructive and constructive waves

- In a **destructive wave**, the swash is weak and the backwash strong. Material is dragged into the sea, eroding the coast. Destructive waves have high energy, and occur in stormy conditions.
- In a **constructive wave**, material is deposited, building up the coast.

  See the diagram on page 6.

  Constructive waves have lower energy and occur in calm conditions.

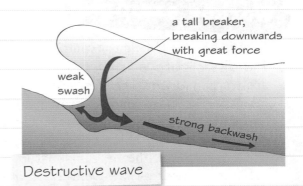

a tall breaker, breaking downwards with great force

weak swash

strong backwash

Destructive wave

Now try this

Identify **two** landforms found along a discordant coast.

(2 marks)

UK weather and climate

The unpredictability of the UK's weather and climate affects rates of coastal erosion and coastal retreat, impacting on landforms and landscapes.

In this component you must study **two** of Coastal, River and Glaciated landscapes. **Only revise this section if it is one of the two you have studied.**

Places most at risk from coastal flooding in England and Wales.

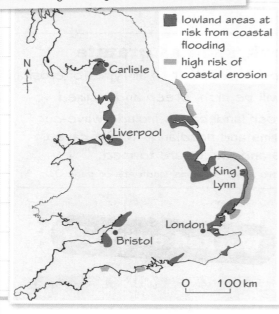

- ■ lowland areas at risk from coastal flooding
- ▨ high risk of coastal erosion

Carlisle, Liverpool, King's Lynn, London, Bristol

0   100 km

Seasonality

The four seasons have different impacts on coastal erosion. For example, cold temperatures in winter lead to freeze–thaw weathering (see page 5) in cliffs.

The effects of stormy weather

Storm frequency is high in many parts of the UK.

✓ Coasts are often subject to strong winds, increasing the eroding power of the waves, and heavy rainfall contributes to mass movement (see page 5).

✓ Frequent storms can damage coastal landforms like spits. Spurn Head along the Holderness coast (see page 13) is at risk of being cut off from the mainland.

✓ Beach sediment can be removed from a section of coastline.

✓ Sand dunes can be removed by storms.

Prevailing winds

Prevailing winds in the UK are from the south-west. This brings warm, moist air from the Atlantic and frequent rainfall, which contributes to weathering and mass movement (see page 5) on the coast.

prevailing winds (south-westerly)

Definitions

Coastal erosion – the breaking down and removal of material along the coast

Coastal retreat – when coastal erosion causes the coastline to move further inland

This is a good answer which uses accurate specialist terminology on how the UK climate contributes to coastal erosion.

Worked example

Explain how the UK climate contributes to coastal erosion.   **(4 marks)**

The UK's climate is temperate maritime, which means winters are mild and wet and summers are warm and wet. The prevailing winds from the south-west often bring rainfall to the country. The large amount of rainfall causes coastlines to be eroded through weathering, and can lead to mass movement and cliff collapse, which lead to coastal retreat. Storm frequency is high, which brings heavy rainfall and strong winds that increase the erosional power of waves. The seasonal nature of the climate means that rocks on the coast are subject to freeze–thaw weathering in winter, which adds to erosion.

Now try this

Explain **one** way in which UK storms can impact on coastal landforms.   **(2 marks)**

Erosional landforms

There are distinctive landforms caused by coastal erosion, including headlands and bays, headland features and wave-cut platforms.

Headlands and bays

These develop on coastlines with a mix of hard and soft rock. They often occur where cliffs have fault lines or joints.

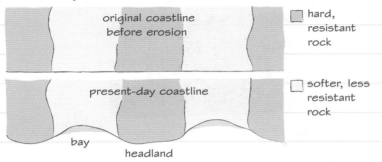

original coastline before erosion

☐ hard, resistant rock

present-day coastline

☐ softer, less resistant rock

bay

headland

Hard rocks like chalk are often left jutting out in the sea, forming **headlands**. Soft rocks such as sands are eroded more quickly, forming **bays**.

> In this component you must study **two** of Coastal, River and Glaciated landscapes. **Only revise this section if it is one of the two you have studied.**

Cliffs

Cliffs are common coastal features. Cliffs are shaped through **weathering** and **erosion**. Soft rock erodes easily to create gently sloping cliffs. Hard rock erodes more slowly to create steep cliffs.

Caves, arches and stacks

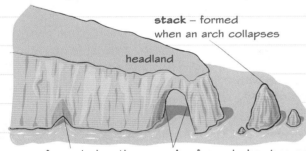

stack – formed when an arch collapses

headland

cave – formed when the waves erode a weakness in the rock such as a joint or a fault

arch – formed when two caves erode back from either side of a headland and meet in the middle

Wave-cut platforms

The erosion of cliffs can create wave-cut platforms – areas of flat rock at the base of the cliff.

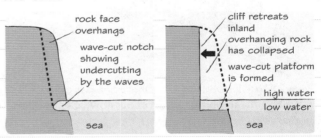

rock face overhangs

wave-cut notch showing undercutting by the waves

sea

cliff retreats inland overhanging rock has collapsed

wave-cut platform is formed

high water
low water

sea

Worked example

Study the OS map of Swanage to the right.
Identify a headland.   **(1 mark)**

Peveril Point

> When identifying a feature on an OS map, remember to look for name evidence – the word 'point' refers to a headland.

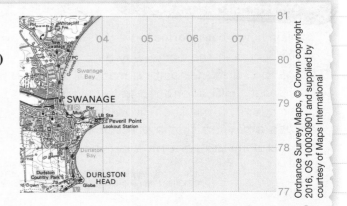

> When explaining the formation of a coastal landform remember to include at least one named coastal process in your answer.

Now try this

Explain how a stack is formed.   **(4 marks)**

9

Depositional landforms

The process of deposition causes the formation of distinctive landforms including beaches, spits and bars.

In this component you must study **two** of Coastal, River and Glaciated landscapes. **Only revise this section if it is one of the two you have studied.**

Beaches

Beaches are accumulations of sand and shingle formed by deposition and shaped by erosion, transportation and deposition.

Beaches can be straight or curved. Curved beaches are formed by waves refracting, or bending, as they enter a bay.

Beaches can be sandy or pebbly (shingle). Shingle beaches are usually found where cliffs are being eroded and where waves are powerful. Ridges in a beach parallel to the sea are called berms and the one highest up the beach shows where the highest tide reaches.

Spits

material moved along beach in a zigzag way by longshore drift

coastline changes direction

spit curved with change of wind direction

spit

prevailing winds bring waves in at an angle

material deposited in shallow, calm water, to form a spit

Spits are narrow beaches of sand or shingle that are attached to the land at one end. They extend across a bay or estuary or where the coastline changes direction. They are formed by longshore drift powered by a strong prevailing wind.

On an OS map spits are shown by a stretch of beach that carries on past the main coastline. They are thin and normally curved in shape.

Worked example

Explain how a bar is formed. **(4 marks)**

A bar forms in the same way as a spit, with longshore drift depositing material away from the coast, until a long ridge is built up. But, unlike a spit, a bar then grows all the way across a bay, so that a stretch of water is cut off and dammed to form a lagoon.

Ordnance Survey Maps, © Crown copyright 2016, OS 100030901 and supplied by courtesy of Maps International

Now try this

Your answer should include both **how** and **why** beach material is transported and deposited.

Explain how beaches are formed.

(4 marks)

Human activity

The ways in which humans use coastal environments can change landscapes, affecting people and the environment.

> In this component you must study **two** of Coastal, River and Glaciated landscapes. **Only revise this section if it is one of the two you have studied.**

Urbanisation
- 👎 Weight of buildings makes cliffs more vulnerable
- 👎 Changes to drainage increase soil saturation
- 👍 Raises interest in protecting coastal landscapes

Agriculture
- 👎 Increases soil erosion
- 👎 Increases sedimentation
- 👍 Creates wildlife habitats

Industry
- 👎 Increases air, noise and visual pollution
- 👎 Can destroy habitats for birds, animals and sealife
- 👍 Brings wealth and jobs to an area

Coastal recession and flooding

- Wildlife habitats destroyed
- Cliffs become dangerous for walkers
- Disruption to communication networks – roads and railway lines – creating difficulties for commuters
- Loss of people's homes
- **Effects of coastal recession and flooding**
- Decreasing value of properties and difficulties in obtaining home insurance
- Increased deposition further along the coast
- Loss of businesses (caravan parks, cafes, golf courses) from disappearing cliffs

> **Coastal recession** is another term for **coastal retreat.**

Worked example

Explain how coastal recession and flooding can affect people. **(4 marks)**

One of the ways coastal recession can affect people is through the loss of homes. Many of the villages on the edge of the UK coastline are disappearing, losing homes to the power of the sea. Transport systems can be disrupted and damaged, especially important railways that run along coastlines. This prevents people from making journeys or means long detours are needed, which cost time and money. Farmers lose valuable farmland due to coastal recession, which means they lose income. In areas where homes have been flooded, people may have to pay more for home insurance, making it more expensive to live there.

> When you are asked to explain, make sure you don't just describe. Here, the student has said **how** coastal recession and flooding can affect people.

Now try this

Explain how industry has affected the coastal environment. **(4 marks)**

Coastal management

There are advantages and disadvantages to different coastal management techniques and these need to be given careful consideration because of the changes that can happen to the landscape.

Soft or hard techniques can alter wave patterns, resulting in increased erosion further along the coast.

> In this component you must study **two** of Coastal, River and Glaciated landscapes. **Only revise this section if it is one of the two you have studied.**

Hard engineering

Many hard engineering techniques can spoil the visual landscape.

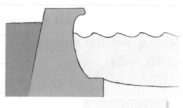

Sea wall

Groynes

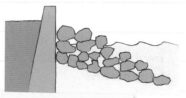

Rip rap defences

👍 Protects cliffs and buildings

👎 More expensive – £5000 – £10 000/m

👍 Prevent sea removing sand

👎 Exposes other coastal areas

👍 Cheaper – £2000/m of timber

👍 Rocks absorb wave energy

👍 Cheaper – £1000 – £3000/m

Soft engineering

This approach aims to work with nature to help maintain the coastline.

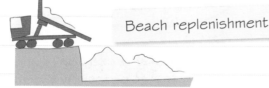

Beach replenishment

Offshore reef e.g. Bournemouth

👍 Sand reduces wave energy

👍 Maintains tourism

👍 Cheaper – £2000/m

👍 Waves break on reef and lose power

👎 May interfere with fishing

👎 More expensive – £5000/m

> Look at the marks. Part (a) just says 'identify' for 1 mark, but part (b) asks you to 'explain' for 2 marks.

This photo shows coastal management at Hornsea in Yorkshire.

a Identify the coastal management feature at A. **(1 mark)**

Groyne

b Explain how coastal management feature B protects the coastline. **(2 marks)**

Feature B is rip rap. The rocks prevent damage to the sea wall by absorbing wave power and trapping beach sand.

> This question is asking for only one advantage and one disadvantage of the technique. Make sure you explain your choices clearly.

Now try this

Explain **one** advantage and **one** disadvantage of using groynes as a form of coastal management. **(4 marks)**

Holderness coast

 Located example You need to know how the interaction of physical and human processes is causing change on one named coastal landscape, including the significance of its location.

Holderness coast, East Yorkshire coastline

Significance of location

- Soft boulder clay is easily eroded, susceptible to slumping after heavy rainfall; chalk is more resistant (Flamborough Head).
- Exposed to strong waves (fetch) from North Sea.

Physical processes at work

- **Coastal erosion** – a combination of strong waves (especially during storms) and rock type ensure the coast is eroded rapidly.
- **Mass movement** – clay frequently slumps from the cliffs after rainfall.
- **Transport** – strong waves move the eroded material away from the coastline; **deposition** happens further south (Spurn Head).

Human processes at work

- Hard engineering on parts of coast (e.g. rip rap and groynes at Mappleton) have protected areas from **erosion** and cliff collapse.
- Hard engineering in some places has prevented **transport**, making erosion worse in other places.

Changes caused

- Some parts are undergoing **coastal retreat** at a rate of nearly 2 m/year.
- Farmland, property and settlements have been lost to the sea, changing the landscape permanently.

Is the coastal landscape you have studied concordant or discordant? (See page 7 for definitions.)

In this component you must study **two** of Coastal, River and Glaciated landscapes. Only revise this section if it is one of the two you have studied.

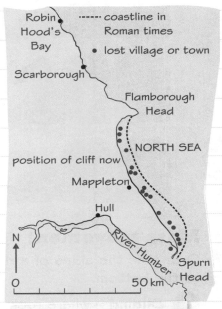

The Holderness coast

Worked example

Using **one** named example, explain **two** ways in which human processes and physical processes have worked together to change a coastal landscape.   **(4 marks)**

On the Holderness coast in East Yorkshire, hard engineering methods including rip rap and groynes have slowed down the rate of coastal erosion and cliff collapse, which would otherwise have been fairly rapid. However, the rip rap and groynes in some places, such as Mappleton, have prevented the transport of material further along the coast, leaving other areas more exposed to erosion by the sea than they would have been and therefore speeding up the rate of coastal retreat.

This is a good answer because it refers to **both** coastal erosion **and** the way people have tried to prevent it happening.

Now try this

Explain the most important factors that have changed a named coastal landscape.   **(4 marks)**

Physical processes 1

Two of the physical processes that shape a river landscape are weathering and mass movement.

> In this component you must study **two** of Coastal, River and Glaciated landscapes. **Only revise this section if it is one of the two you have studied.**

Weathering processes

Weathering is the wearing away in situ of the river valley sides. There are three weathering processes common to river valleys.

1 **Mechanical** (freeze–thaw)

Water fills a crack or joint in the rock.

Water freezes and the crack is widened.

Repeated freeze–thaw action increases the size of the crack until the block of rock breaks off.

Loose blocks of rock are called **scree**.

2 **Chemical** (acid rain)

Rainwater is slightly acidic. The acid reacts with minerals in the rocks and dissolves them. For example, granite contains feldspar, which is converted into soft clay minerals as a result of a chemical reaction with water.

3 **Biological**

> Acids released by vegetation speed up chemical weathering.

Roots grow into cracks and split rocks apart.

Mass movement

Over time the sides of a river valley become less steep as material is moved from the top to the bottom.

1 **Sliding** – where rock, weathered or eroded material or earth moves down a slope. Gravity pulls the weakened material quickly downwards.

2 **Slumping** – where the river erodes the bottom of the valley slope, making it steeper. Material above slides downwards, particularly if it is saturated with rainwater.

Worked example

Explain how mechanical weathering can affect river valleys. **(3 marks)**

> The command word here is **explain**. Make sure that you give the **reasons** for how the process will cause change.

When it rains, water falls into cracks in the rock and freezes when the temperature drops below zero. This causes the water to expand and put pressure on the surrounding rock. The repeated process of freezing and melting over time causes fragments of rock to break off and can lead to rock falls, steepening the valley sides and forming scree slopes.

Now try this

Mass movement can occur in river valleys. Explain **one** process of mass movement. **(3 marks)**

Physical processes 2

Erosion, transport and deposition are also physical processes that shape a river landscape.

In this component you must study **two** of Coastal, River and Glaciated landscapes. Only revise this section if it is one of the two you have studied.

Erosion

Hydraulic action
The force of the water on the bed and banks of the river removes material

Attrition
The load that is carried by the river bumps together and wears down into smaller, smoother pieces

Solution
Some rock minerals dissolve in river water (e.g. calcium carbonate in limestone)

Abrasion
Material carried by the river rubs against the bed and banks and wears them away

Transport and deposition

Transport is the way in which the river carries eroded material or load.

There are four main types of transportation: **traction**, **saltation**, **suspension** and **solution**.

When the river slows down it loses energy and may drop some of its load. This is called **deposition**.

See page 19 for depositional features.

Traction
Large boulders are rolled along the river bed

Saltation
Smaller pebbles are bounced along the river bed, picked up then dropped as the river flow changes

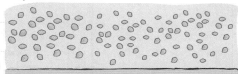

Suspension
Finer sand and silt particles are carried along in the flow, giving the river a brown appearance

Solution
Some minerals, such as chalk, are dissolved in the water and carried along in the flow, although they cannot be seen

Worked example

Explain how a river will transport eroded material. **(2 marks)**

One way a river can transport eroded material is through traction. This is where the river's flow rolls large boulders along the river bed.

When you are asked about a specific process, remember to give the name of the process.

Now try this

Compare the processes of hydraulic action and attrition. **(4 marks)**

When **comparing**, make sure you include both similarities and differences between your key words. You can use the word 'whereas' to make it clear you are answering the question.

15

River valley changes

Rivers, and the valleys they flow in, change in different ways between their source (where they start) and their mouth (where they join the sea).

Only revise this section if you studied River landscapes.

River profile

A river's long profile shows the height and distance downstream from the river's source to its mouth. It is a curved shape, steeper near the source and flatter near the mouth.

You will need to know how one named UK river changes between its upper, middle and lower course.

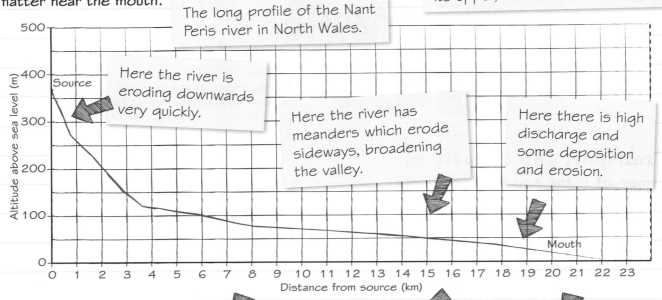

The long profile of the Nant Peris river in North Wales.

Here the river is eroding downwards very quickly.

Here the river has meanders which erode sideways, broadening the valley.

Here there is high discharge and some deposition and erosion.

	Upper course	Middle course	Lower course
Gradient	steep	less steep	shallow gradient
Discharge	small	large	very large
Depth	shallow	deeper	deep
Channel shape	narrow, steep sides	flat, steep sides	flat floor, gently sloping sides
Velocity	quite fast	fast	very fast
Valley profile	steep sides	flat with steep sides	flat with gently sloping sides
Features	waterfalls, interlocking spurs	meanders, floodplain	meanders, floodplain, levées, ox-bow lakes
Sediment size and shape	angular boulders	more rounded rocks	smooth, rounded pebbles

Worked example

Explain **one** difference between the shape of a river valley in its upper and lower course. **(2 marks)**

In the upper course the river valley has steep sides due to the river eroding downwards, whereas in the lower course the valley is flatter, with gently sloping sides, as the river erodes horizontally.

When a question asks for a named river, write about the river you have studied.

Now try this

For a named UK river, explain how the characteristics change from its upper to its lower course. **(6 marks)**

Weather and climate challenges

The UK's weather and climate have an effect on river processes, causing changes to landforms and landscapes.

Impact of climate on rivers

In this component you must study **two** of Coastal, River and Glaciated landscapes. Only revise this section if it is one of the two you have studied.

Erosion rate will be higher with greater discharge, so rivers in wet climates will erode more material than those in dry climates, widening and deepening river valleys and increasing the amount of eroded sediment.

Impact of climate on river landforms and landscapes

Amount of discharge is affected by climate. Wetter climates mean greater discharge. Hotter temperatures mean greater evaporation so less discharge. The greater the discharge, the higher the velocity of the river.

Transport rate will be greater where the energy of the water is greater, so rivers in wet climates will transport more material than those in dry climates.

Weathering of rocks will be greater in some climates: for example, freeze–thaw weathering increases where temperatures range from just above to just below freezing.

Changing weather

The UK has experienced some extreme weather in recent years. This can increase the risk of river flooding due to:

- **increasing frequency of storms** – more periods of heavy, intense rainfall meaning more water flowing into rivers, which then overflow

- **increasing periods of hot, dry weather** – bakes the upper soil so when it does rain the water runs off the surface, it can't soak in, reaching rivers and rapidly increasing discharge

- **soil becoming impermeable during cold conditions** – snowmelt cannot infiltrate and flows rapidly into rivers, increasing flood risk.

Worked example

Remember for an **explain** question you need to say **why** something occurs.

Explain the impact that storms can have on river landforms.   **(4 marks)**

Storms can cause a sudden increase in river discharge and velocity. This increases the rate of erosion and sediment transport and means that landforms (for example, river valleys) will be widened and deepened by increased hydraulic action and abrasion. The river can flood and sediment is deposited on the floodplain. This raises the height of the floodplain and the levées, which are immediately parallel to the river.

Now try this

Remember to be very accurate when reading information from graphs.

Study the annual rainfall graph for Birsay.

1   Which year had the highest rainfall?   **(1 mark)**

2   Suggest **one** impact this high rainfall might have on the discharge of rivers in the area.
   (2 marks)

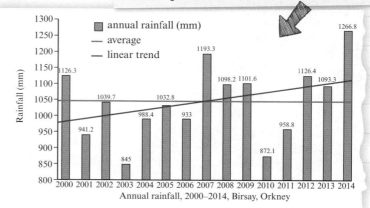

Annual rainfall, 2000–2014, Birsay, Orkney

Upper course landscape

Interlocking spurs, waterfalls, gorges and river cliffs are formed by erosion processes and the influence of geology in the upper course of the river.

> In this component you must study **two** of Coastal, River and Glaciated landscapes. **Only revise this section if it is one of the two you have studied.**

Landforms

In the upper course, the river erodes vertically (downwards). The **gradient** is steep and the **channel** is narrow.

Interlocking spurs

The river at its source is small and has limited energy. It flows naturally from side to side, around ridges in the valley sides, called spurs. The spurs become interlocking with those on the other side of the valley.

Waterfalls

Waterfalls are a common feature in the upper course of a river, where there is an increase in vertical erosion. They form where there is a layer of hard, resistant rock (the cap rock) overlying a softer, less resistant rock.

interlocking spurs

river channel

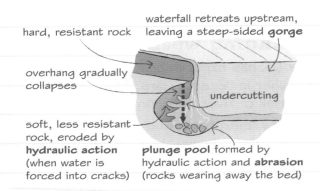

hard, resistant rock

waterfall retreats upstream, leaving a steep-sided **gorge**

overhang gradually collapses

undercutting

soft, less resistant rock, eroded by **hydraulic action** (when water is forced into cracks)

plunge pool formed by hydraulic action and **abrasion** (rocks wearing away the bed)

Gorges

Over a long time, the process of undercutting and collapse is repeated, and the waterfall retreats, forming a steep-sided gorge.

Avon Gorge

Worked example

Look at the diagram opposite.
Explain how river cliffs form. **(2 marks)**

River cliffs form on the outer side of the meander, when the faster water velocity laterally erodes the riverbank. They are usually almost vertical.

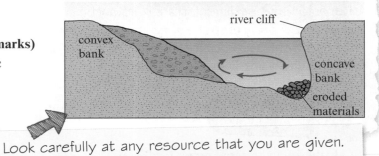

convex bank

river cliff

concave bank

eroded materials

Look carefully at any resource that you are given.

Now try this

Examine how physical processes work together to form the waterfalls shown on the map extract. **(8 marks)**

Remember to provide a well-balanced answer with explanations of physical processes and use relevant geographical terms.

Lower course landscape 1

Depositional processes in the lower course of the river produce distinctive landforms – **floodplains**, **levées** and **point bars**.

Floodplains

A floodplain is the wide, flat area of land either side of a river and experiences floods when the river tops its banks.

> In the lower course, the river is nearing the sea and carries a huge amount of sediment (**alluvium**).

> When the river floods, excess water spills over the surrounding area.

> During flooding, the **velocity** of the river is reduced, it loses energy, and deposits sediment, forming the floodplain.

> The floodplain is shaped by the **lateral** erosion of meanders as they gradually migrate downstream and by deposition of material on the inner bends.

In this component you must study **two** of Coastal, River and Glaciated landscapes. **Only revise this section if it is one of the two you have studied.**

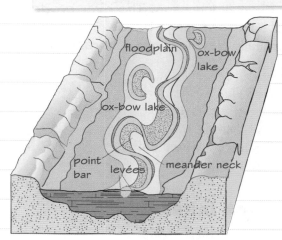

floodplain, ox-bow lake, ox-bow lake, point bar, levées, meander neck

How levées develop

The **deposition** process, which takes place during flooding, continues until eventually embankments, made of larger, heavier sediment, are created beside the river. These are called **levées**.

before a flood   during a flood   after a flood

When flooding occurs, the heaviest material is deposited first due to the decrease in the river's energy. This material creates natural embankments called levées.

The smaller and finer sediment, or alluvium, is deposited further from the river because it requires less energy to carry it.

Worked example

Study the photo opposite.

a Name the landform X.   **(1 mark)**

Point bar

b Explain how this landform formed.   **(3 marks)**

Point bars are formed by deposition. On the inside bends of meanders, the river current is relatively slow and therefore low energy. This means that the river is not able to transport its load due to low velocity and the load is deposited on the inside bend. Over time the deposits of sand, silt and pebbles build up to form a point bar.

Sketching river landforms from photographs will help you to recognise them.

Now try this

Study the cross-section diagram, which shows a river landform. Explain how landform X formed.

(3 marks)

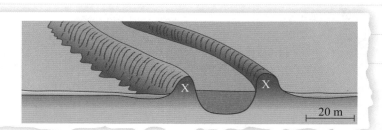

20 m

Lower course landscape 2

Meanders and ox-bow lakes are landforms created by the interaction of deposition and erosion processes in the middle and lower courses of a river.

> Only revise this section if you studied River landscapes.

Meanders

In the middle course, the **width**, **depth** and **velocity** of the river all increase. The river erodes laterally (sideways) and starts to form large bends. The bends get bigger and wider, and eventually develop into a horseshoe shape called a **meander**.

> On the inner bend of a meander, where the current is slower, there is greater deposition, creating a **point bar**.

> On the outer bend of a meander, where the current is faster, there is greater **erosion**. This wears away the bank creating a **river cliff**.

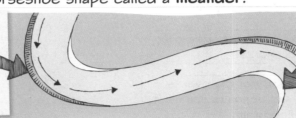

Ox-bow lakes

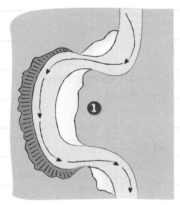
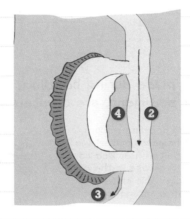
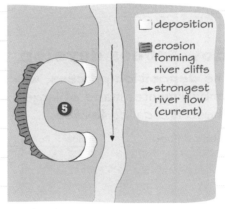

☐ deposition
▨ erosion forming river cliffs
→ strongest river flow (current)

① Narrow neck of meander is gradually being eroded.

③ Deposition takes place, sealing off the old meander.

⑤ **Ox-bow lake** left behind when meander completely cut off.

② Water now takes the quickest route.

④ Meander neck has been cut through completely.

Worked example

Identify the river landform shown at grid square 3109 on the map.

☐ **A** Waterfall
☐ **B** Ox-bow lake
☒ **C** Meander
☐ **D** Levée

(1 mark)

Ordnance Survey Maps, © Crown copyright 2016, OS 100030901 and supplied by courtesy of Maps International

Now try this

Using this floodplain diagram, examine how the interaction of processes causes the formation of a meander. **(8 marks)**

broad floodplain
point bar
river cliff
point bar
floodplain
bluff
current of fastest flow

Make sure you don't just describe the processes, but say how they **interact**.

Human activity

Human activities and changes in land use – urbanisation, agriculture and industry – can affect rivers and change river landscapes.

In this component you must study **two** of Coastal, River and Glaciated landscapes. **Only revise this section if it is one of the two you have studied.**

Urbanisation

☑ Urbanisation has caused towns to grow, meaning there are fewer **permeable** surfaces. Water flows into the rivers, increasing discharge.

☑ Increasing demand for housing has led to new houses being built on **floodplains**. This changes the natural landscape.

☑ Rivers may be channelised or made to flow underground to make room for urban developments. If this happens, erosion and deposition cannot take place.

Agriculture

☑ Field drains can improve farmland, but quickly move water into streams and rivers, and can destroy natural wetland landscapes.

☑ Forests can be felled to make way for farmland. Trees intercept rainfall, helping to reduce **surface run-off**. Removing trees means water reaches rivers more quickly.

☑ Abstracting water for irrigation reduces the flow and velocity of a river so deposition occurs rather than erosion.

☑ Ploughing fields up and down a slope can increase the amount of sediment in rivers and increase deposition.

Industry

☑ Industry is a big user of water, so can reduce the amount of water in rivers, leading to less erosion.

☑ Industrial processes can pollute rivers if chemicals or waste are spilled or dumped into them. This can destroy plants and animals and change the natural landscape.

Chemical works by the River Weaver, Cheshire

Worked example

This answer correctly focuses on land-use impact on rivers, rather than examining river changes in general.

Explain how land-use change can affect rivers. **(4 marks)**

Land-use change can affect rivers in several ways. Changing land from soil to artificial surfaces, such as paving over gardens to create parking spaces on previously green spaces, increases the amount of impermeable surfaces. This means less water can infiltrate into the ground and increases the speed and amount of run-off, so more water reaches the river faster, and increases discharge. Deforestation, another type of land-use change, reduces the amount of interception so rain reaches the ground faster and surface run-off increases. Building on floodplains removes one way that rivers can flood without causing damage, and increases the risk of flooding as the amount of impermeable surfaces increase.

Now try this

Explain how human processes are contributing to river flooding on one named river. **(3 marks)**

Had a look ☐   Nearly there ☐   Nailed it! ☐

Causes and effects of flooding

River flooding is caused by a combination of physical and human factors, and has a range of physical and human effects.

Only revise this section if you studied River landscapes.

Physical causes

Rainfall intensity	Geology	Snowmelt	Drainage basin
A lot of rainfall over a short period of time prevents soil **infiltration**.	Rocks like granite are **impermeable**, so water is unable to **percolate** from the thin soil above.	At spring time warmer temperatures will **melt** snow creating more water.	Steep-sided valleys or a lot of **tributaries** means the water enters the river system quicker.

Excess water will flow towards the river as **surface run-off (overland flow)** or **groundwater**.

Water will reach the river channel more quickly and force the level of river to rise above the bank level. Flooding can then occur.

Worked example

Humans have many impacts on rivers. Explain how these can cause flooding.   **(2 marks)**

Many of these impacts result in excess water flowing towards rivers as surface run-off. This water reaches the river channel more quickly and forces the level of the river to rise above bank level. River flooding can then occur.

Effects of floods

✓ **Physical effects** include landslides, soil erosion, loss of natural habitats, contamination of water supplies.

✓ **Human effects** include death, disease, damage to property, insurance claims, loss of livelihoods, loss of crops and farm animals, disruption to transport.

Now try this

Study the flood hydrograph opposite.

1   Calculate the lag time.   **(1 mark)**

A flood hydrograph (or storm hydrograph) shows how a river responds to a rainstorm.

The lag time is the difference in time between the peak of the rainstorm and the peak of the river discharge.

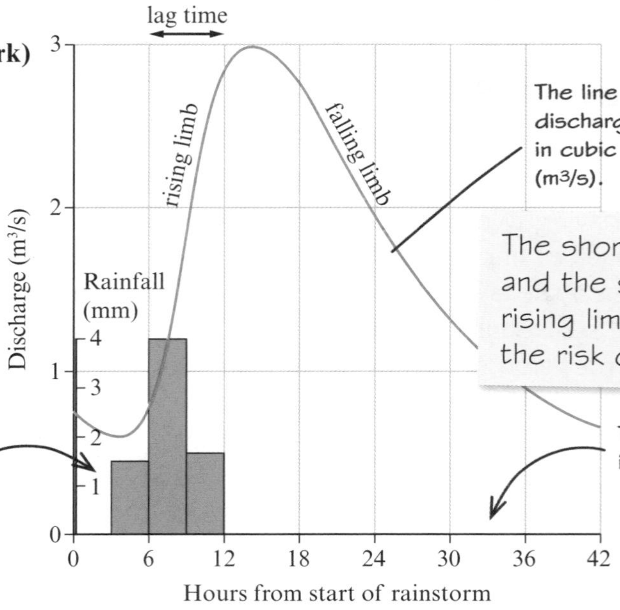

The line graph shows the river discharge. It is measured in cubic metres per second (m^3/s).

The shorter the lag time and the steeper the rising limb, the greater the risk of flooding.

The bar graph shows the amount of rainfall. It is measured in millimetres (mm).

The x-axis shows time in hours.

Flood hydrograph: Discharge (m^3/s) and Rainfall (mm) plotted against Hours from start of rainstorm. Labels include lag time, rising limb, falling limb.

River management

Hard and soft engineering are used to help protect river landscapes from flooding, but each has its advantages and disadvantages.

> In this component you must study **two** of Coastal, River and Glaciated landscapes. Only revise this section if it is one of the two you have studied.

Hard engineering

Hard engineering involves building structures as a defence against flooding.

Dams and reservoirs – barriers constructed to hold back water in artificial lakes:

👍 Store large volumes of water until needed

👍 Long-lasting; can be used to generate hydro-electric power (HEP)

👎 Expensive to build

👎 Sediment can build up in reservoirs

Landscape impact – the natural river valley landscape is flooded.

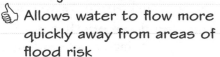

Channelisation – deepening or widening the river channel:

👍 Allows water to flow more quickly away from areas of flood risk

👎 Visually unattractive

👎 More water is taken downstream, increasing the flood risk to other settlements

Landscape impact – replaces the natural meanders and floodplain with an artificial channel.

Soft engineering

Soft engineering uses natural processes to reduce the impacts of river flooding.

Floodplain zoning – prevents development in areas most prone to flooding next to rivers.

👍 Reduces number of homes at risk of flooding

👍 Allows infiltration so surface run-off takes place and flooding is reduced

👎 Restricts the growth of settlements

Landscape impact – preserves the natural floodplain.

Washlands – areas next to rivers that are deliberately flooded to avoid flooding residential or important agricultural areas.

👍 Create an area for floodwater to go

👍 Allow natural river processes such as deposition

👎 Might limit the use of land

Landscape impact – preserves the natural floodplain landscapes in the mid and lower river courses.

Worked example

> Remember to give different types of advantage and disadvantage – not just opposites.

Study the photograph. Explain **one** advantage and **one** disadvantage of channelisation of a river. **(4 marks)**

One advantage of channelisation is that the friction between the water and the channel sides is reduced. This means that water moves rapidly away from areas that could otherwise flood. One disadvantage is that this rapid increase in water velocity will erode and flood areas downstream from the channelised section of the river.

Now try this

> Remember to use linking words like 'whereas' when you talk about differences.

Explain the differences between hard and soft engineering. **(4 marks)**

River Dee, Wales

 Located example

You need to know a located example of the significance of an upland or lowland river landscape.

> In this component you must study **two** of Coastal, River and Glaciated landscapes. **Only revise this section if it is one of the two you have studied.**

How the River Dee landscape was formed

- The source of the River Dee is Dduallt, an upland area in Snowdonia, North Wales.
- Here annual precipitation is very high.
- The Dee flows south-easterly, eroding this heavily glaciated upland landscape formed of igneous and metamorphic rocks.

- Near Chester the river meanders across a wide floodplain, eroding softer sedimentary rocks and depositing sediment.
- A section is artificially straightened, giving a man-made landscape.
- Further deposition occurs to form the Wirral estuarine landscape.

1732–1736 – channelisation of 8 km improved navigation, increasing discharge and velocity and creating an artificial landscape.

Under the River Dee Regulation Scheme a series of reservoirs was built, e.g. Llyn Celyn.

Floodplain landscape between Holt and Worthenbury with meanders, alluvium and river terrace deposits formed by active erosion and deposition, causing the river to change its course over time.

Human factors causing change

Physical factors causing change

Earth embankments were built along the middle course to protect agricultural land and properties, preventing further development of the floodplain landscape.

If sea levels rise by 1 m by the year 2100, coastal landscapes will replace salt- and freshwater marsh landscapes.

In the Dee Estuary, rises in sea level will destroy the estuary landscape.

Worked example

> For this question, it is important to provide **two clear** factors in your answer.

Explain **two** factors that have changed the natural course of one UK river. **(4 marks)**

One of the factors that has changed the natural course of the River Dee in Wales is channelisation of 8 km of the river's course during the 1730s. The channel was straightened to improve navigation but this has increased both the discharge and velocity, increasing the risk of flooding further downstream. A second factor is the construction of reservoirs e.g. the Llyn Celyn under the RDRS (River Dee Regulation Scheme). This has increased storage of water, which has altered the course of the river by creating artificial wide, deep lakes.

Now try this

For a named UK river you have studied, evaluate how the interaction of physical and human factors is causing changes to the landscape. **(8 marks)**

> Remember that **evaluate** means you need to **review** the importance of both physical and human factors and make a clear **conclusion**.

Glacial processes

A range of physical processes work together to shape glaciated upland landscapes.

Only revise this section if you studied Glaciated landscapes.

Glacial erosion

This was important in the past when glaciers shaped UK upland landscapes.

Freeze–thaw weathering is still taking place in glaciated upland areas today.

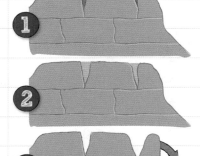

1 Water fills a crack or joint in rock.

2 Water freezes and expands, and the crack widens.

3 Repeated freeze–thaw action increases size of crack until block breaks off – loose blocks form **scree**.

Abrasion and plucking

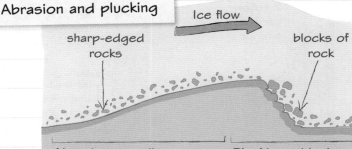

Abrasion – small, sharp-edged rocks embedded in the base of the glacier wear away the bedrock underneath. Larger rock fragments cause scrapes, called **striations**.

Plucking – blocks of loosened bedrock freeze to the base of the glacier and get pulled out as the glacier moves down the valley.

Transport and deposition

Glaciers move in two ways:

- **basal sliding** – meltwater at glacier base acts as a lubricant; glacier moves downhill.
- **internal flow** – ice crystals **within** glacier slide over each other, changing shape and size.

Glacial **deposition** occurs mainly when ice melts:

- **fluvioglacial material** – sediments deposited by streams flowing from the melting glacier
- **till deposits** – material deposited directly by ice.

Post-glacial processes

Glaciated landscapes are still being changed by freeze–thaw action and mass movement:

- **soil movement** – slow downward movement of saturated soil particles due to gravity. Frost action weakens soil structure and groundsoil (possibly still frozen) acts as slip plane
- **rock falls/slides** – fast movement of rocks loosened by freeze–thaw fall from steep glaciated slopes to valley floor.

UK weather and climate

Past climates

- The last important UK glacial period was the Pleistocene, about 12 000 years ago.
- Temperatures fluctuated above and below freezing, causing freeze–thaw weathering and glacial erosion.
- **Accumulation** was greater than **ablation** (melting) in winter (increased snowfall, less melting) so glaciers advanced.
- As temperatures increased at the end of the Pleistocene, ablation was greater than accumulation in summer due to ice melt, so glaciers retreated.

Worked example

Explain **two** ways present-day weather and climate affect processes that impact on glaciated upland landscapes in the UK. **(4 marks)**

The weather changes with the seasons, so in the winter freeze-thaw weathering occurs, producing scree slopes. Temperatures also vary above and below freezing over a 24-hour period, which increases the rate of freeze-thaw weathering.

Now try this

State the name given to the loose blocks of rock broken off during freeze-thaw weathering. **(1 mark)**

Erosional landforms 1

Some of the distinctive landforms in glaciated upland landscapes formed as a result of erosion. These include corries, tarns, arêtes, pyramidal peaks and roches moutonnées.

Only revise this section if you studied Glaciated landscapes.

Corries and tarns

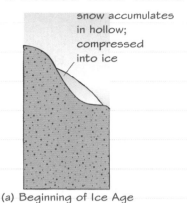

snow accumulates in hollow; compressed into ice

(a) Beginning of Ice Age

freeze–thaw above glacier
plucking steepens the back wall
moraine left at end of glacier
glacier
maximum erosion where weight of ice is greatest
moraine
abrasion deepens the hollow
rate of erosion decreases

(b) During Ice Age

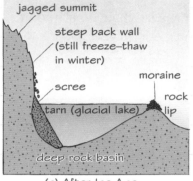

jagged summit
steep back wall (still freeze–thaw in winter)
moraine
scree
rock lip
tarn (glacial lake)
deep rock basin

(c) After Ice Age

Arêtes

Arêtes are knife-edged ridges. They form when two corries form back to back. Freeze–thaw weathering and glacial erosion make the ridge narrower and steeper.

Tarns/glacial lakes

Tarns (**corrie** lakes) are roughly circular pools found in the bottom of a corrie deepened by a glacier. After the glacier melted, rain or river water filled the corrie. Deposited moraine or a rock lip may form a natural dam at the edge.

Roches moutonnées

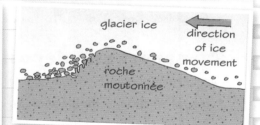

glacier ice
direction of ice movement
roche moutonnée

Roches moutonnées are asymmetric landforms where abrasion has smoothed the 'stoss' (upstream) side of the rock and plucking has roughened the 'lee' (downstream) side.

Worked example

Using this map extract, label a corrie and an arête. **(2 marks)**

corrie

arête

Ordnance Survey Maps, © Crown copyright 2016, OS 100030901 and supplied by courtesy of Maps International

Now try this

Name the feature found in the corrie hollow shown on the map extract in the Worked example.

(1 mark)

This map is from the Ordnance Survey Landranger series, map 115, 1:50 000 scale

Erosional landforms 2

Other landforms formed by erosion in glaciated upland landscapes occur in valleys. These include truncated spurs, glacial troughs and hanging valleys.

In this component you must study **two** of Coastal, River and Glaciated landscapes. **Only revise this section if it is one of the two you have studied.**

Glacial troughs

Distinctive U-shaped glacial troughs are easily recognised on OS maps.

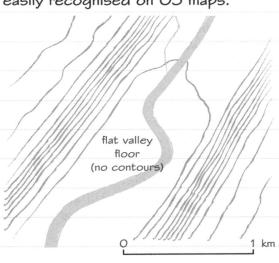

flat valley floor (no contours)

0   1 km

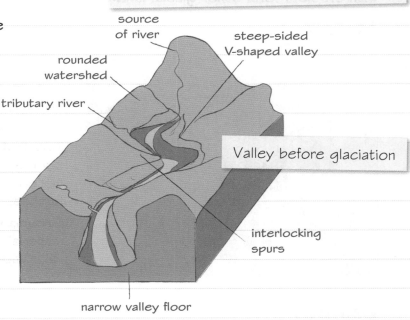

source of river

steep-sided V-shaped valley

rounded watershed

tributary river

Valley before glaciation

interlocking spurs

narrow valley floor

Truncated spurs are formed when the material transported by the glacier (moraine) erodes the lower sections of interlocking spurs.

A hanging valley is a smaller, side valley left 'hanging' above the main valley. The main glacier erodes a deeper glacial trough and a tributary glacier (often following a tributary river valley) erodes a less deep trough, which is found higher up the steep sides of the main trough. There is often a waterfall from the edge of the hanging valley into the main glacial trough.

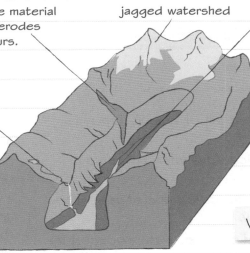

jagged watershed

A glacial trough is a large U-shaped valley with steep sides and a flat floor. The glacier changes the shape of the valley from a V-shaped river valley to a U-shaped glaciated valley by the processes of abrasion and plucking. Frequently, long thin lakes called **ribbon lakes** form in glacial troughs.

Valley after glaciation

Worked example

Study the photo. Which of the following is the glacial erosion feature shown in the photo? **(1 mark)**

☐ **A** Corrie
☒ **B** Hanging valley
☐ **C** Tarn
☐ **D** Roche moutonnée

 With multiple-choice questions, always take time to double-check your answer.

Now try this

Explain how hanging valleys are formed. **(3 marks)**

Transport and depositional landforms

Transport and deposition (sometimes interacting with erosion) form other glacial landforms.

Moraines

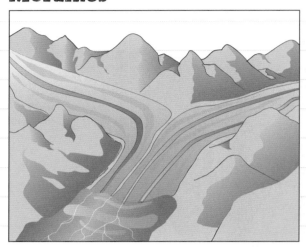

In this component you must study **two** of Coastal, River and Glaciated landscapes. **Only revise this section if it is one of the two you have studied.**

Glaciers transport different types of weathered and eroded material. When the glacier melts, this is deposited in piles or ridges called **moraines**.

Terminal (end) **moraine** – most deposition occurs at the **snout**, where great ridges of material pile up. Terminal moraines mark the furthest extent of the glacier.

Ground moraine – as the glacier melts it drops material known as **boulder clay** or **till** all over the valley floor. This leaves hummocky ground behind.

Drumlin

stoss
drumlins
lee

Direction of ice flow ⟶

- A **drumlin** is an elongated hill of glacial deposits, shaped like an egg.
- Drumlins form beneath ice advancing across a lowland area.
- The blunt end of a drumlin, called the **stoss**, faces the direction of ice flow.
- The tapered end, called the **lee**, was produced by erosion and points in the direction of glacial flow.
- A series of drumlins across the landscape is called a swarm or a basket of eggs.

Crag and tail

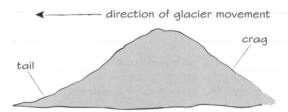

⟵ direction of glacier movement

crag

tail

A **crag and tail** is a landform consisting of a rock hill and a tapering ridge. It forms when a glacier is forced to flow over and around a band of resistant rock. Erosion steepens the resistant rock, creating the crag; deposition of moraine behind the crag forms the 'tail'.

Worked example

Make sure you **explain** the difference clearly.

Explain the difference between terminal and ground moraine. **(2 marks)**

Terminal moraine is material built up at the end of the glacier, whereas ground moraine is material deposited on the valley floor.

Now try this

Explain how erosion and deposition processes cause the formation of crag and tail. **(3 marks)**

Human activity

Over time glaciated upland landscapes have been shaped by human activity. You will need to know the different types of human activity and the impact these have on glaciated landscapes.

> In this component you must study **two** of Coastal, River and Glaciated landscapes. Only revise this section if it is one of the two you have studied.

Settlements

Few settlements are found in upland glaciated landscapes due the difficulty of building and creating access points on uneven steep terrain. Small settlements tend to be in the valleys, often farming communities with second or holiday homes. Developing these settlements has led to the removal of trees, increasing soil erosion and changing the appearance of the landscape.

Farming and forestry

Arable farming is rare in glaciated uplands, which are used for hill sheep and beef. Hill farming has created field boundaries – fences, walls – and led to the removal of trees. Overgrazing can increase soil erosion.

In some upland areas conifer forests have been planted. This sort of planting can prevent soil erosion but can also unbalance ecosystems, forcing some species out.

Development of glaciated upland landscapes

Water storage and supply: upland glaciated landscapes tend to receive high rainfall. In the UK, glaciated U-shaped valleys have been used to create reservoirs.

👍 Provides water for towns and cities

👎 Construction can destroy natural habitats and plant species

👎 Changes the appearance of the landscape

Recreation and tourism: glaciated landscapes are popular tourist sites for walkers, mountain climbers and mountain biking.

👍 Increase jobs for local people

👎 Walkers can increase soil erosion

👎 Made paths and tracks affect the natural appearance of the landscape

Renewable energy: glaciated landscapes provide opportunities for producing renewable energy. Dams and reservoirs provide HEP; wind turbines can generate energy.

👍 No pollution

👎 Can spoil the look of the natural landscape

Conservation

👍 Conservation helps to protect fragile environments that contain rare plant and wildlife species

👎 Can be expensive to establish and needs ongoing funds to be effective

Worked example

Explain **one** advantage and **one** disadvantage of producing renewable energy in glaciated upland landscapes. **(4 marks)**

Harnessing renewable energy resources in glaciated landscapes, such as dam construction in U-shaped valleys, helps to generate clean energy that doesn't pollute the environment. A disadvantage of HEP production is that glacial troughs are flooded, changing the appearance of the upland landscape and any settlements or farms in the valley will be destroyed.

> This is a good answer because it gives clear advantages and disadvantages and focuses on glaciated upland landscapes.

Now try this

Explain how human activities have impacted on glaciated landscapes. **(4 marks)**

Glacial development

Located example You will need to know the significance of one named UK glaciated upland landscape, how it has been formed and the most significant factors in its change.

In this component you must study **two** of Coastal, River and Glaciated landscapes. **Only revise this section if it is one of the two you have studied.**

Significance of location

✓ Snowdonia is located in North Wales.

✓ It has been a National Park since 1951.

✓ It is an upland mountainous area, with four peaks over 1000 m.

✓ The highest peak is Snowdon.

✓ Geologically there are sedimentary, metamorphic and igneous rocks.

✓ 18 000 years ago Snowdonia was covered by an ice cap.

✓ Weathering processes, the ice cap and smaller glaciers produced a distinct glaciated landscape (see OS map opposite).

✓ As the glaciers melted, glacial deposition took place in lower areas such as glacial troughs.

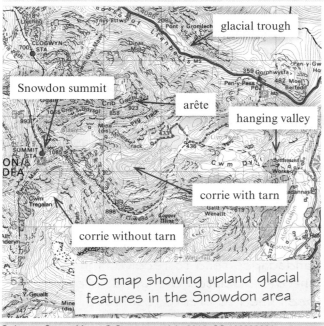

OS map showing upland glacial features in the Snowdon area

Ordnance Survey Maps, © Crown copyright 2016, OS 100030901 and supplied by courtesy of Maps International

Quarrying and mining

Slate quarrying was once an important industry in Snowdonia, but changed the natural landscape. For example, Dinorwic quarry, once one of Snowdonia's biggest slate quarries, has left waste slate tips and terraces – a significant scar on the landscape.

Worked example

Explain how recreation and tourism can cause changes in a named glaciated upland landscape.

(4 marks)

One of the ways tourism can change the natural landscape of glaciated areas is through the volume of tourists who move around the landscape on a yearly basis. Walking is popular in Snowdonia, which has led to increased soil erosion of footpaths, increasing surface run-off. More than 360 000 people walk up Snowdon each year, so a railway and a visitor centre have been built, affecting the natural appearance of this glaciated mountain. Honeypot villages like Betws-y-Coed attract many visitors, increasing noise/air pollution.

Remember to refer to a named landscape you have studied in your answer.

Now try this

Assess how human activities can change glaciated upland landscapes.

(8 marks)

Remember to structure your answer with a balanced argument on how human activities have changed the environment. Use specific details from your located example.

Global atmospheric circulation

The Earth's atmosphere is in constant motion, transferring heat energy around the Earth.

Circulation cells

Different areas of the Earth receive different amounts of solar radiation: there is a surplus of heat energy at the Equator and a deficit at the Poles. Three circulation cells in each hemisphere redistribute this heat energy.

1 At the Equator, warmed air rises to 15 km, causing low pressure. The air current divides, cools and moves north and south to form Hadley cells. The cooled air sinks at 30° north and south of the Equator, leading to high pressure.

2 Some of the cooled air moves back towards the Equator as trade winds. The rest travels towards the Poles, forming the lower part of Ferrel cells.

3 At 60° north and south, the warmer air of the Ferrel cells meets colder polar air. The warmer air rises to form Polar cells. This air travels to the Poles, where it cools and sinks, forming areas of high pressure.

Global circulation cells

cool — Polar cell — Ferrel cell — Polar easterlies — westerly winds — warm — north-east trade winds — Hadley cell — Equator — hot — south-east trade winds — westerly winds — warm — Polar easterlies — cool

The Earth receives all of its heat energy from the Sun – called **solar radiation**.

Oceanic circulation

Ocean currents also transfer heat energy from areas of surplus (Equator) to areas of deficit (Poles). Wind-driven surface currents and deeper ocean currents move warm water towards the Poles and colder water towards the Equator.

In the Arctic and Antarctic, water gets very cold and dense, so it sinks. Warmer water from the Equator replaces this surface water, creating ocean currents, such as the Gulf Stream. Cooled water flows back towards the Equator, forming cold currents, such as the Humboldt Current.

Labrador — E. Greenland — Irminger — N. Atlantic Drift — N. Atlantic Drift — Canary — Gulf Stream — N. Equatorial — Equatorial Counter — Equator

→ = warm ocean current
→ = cold ocean current

Ocean currents in the North Atlantic

Study the diagram opposite. Explain how ocean currents transfer heat energy across the Earth. **(3 marks)**

Colder, denser water at the Poles sinks and flows towards the Equator as cold ocean currents. Less dense water from the equatorial areas flows as warm surface currents to replace this cold water. This process is repeated, causing heat energy to be transferred from the Equator to the Poles.

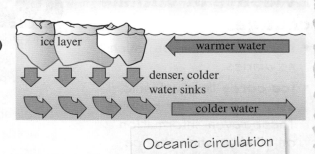

ice layer — warmer water — denser, colder water sinks — colder water

Oceanic circulation

Describe how atmospheric circulation transfers heat energy from the Equator to the polar regions. **(2 marks)**

Natural climate change

The average climatic conditions of the Earth change naturally over time, creating both warmer and colder periods.

The Quaternary period

The Quaternary period covers the last 2.6 million years, when there have been:

- more than 60 cold periods with ice advances, lasting about 100 000 years
- warmer interglacial periods lasting about 15 000 years.

Recent temperature changes

In the last 250 years the Earth's temperature has risen significantly compared to before. Average temperature in the middle of the last Ice Age was about 5 °C below today's average temperature.

Global climate has changed over different timescales

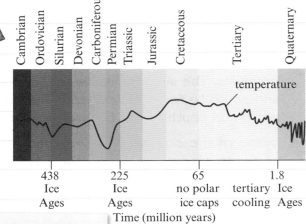

We are currently living in an interglacial period.

Milankovitch cycles

These are long-term changes to the Earth's orbit and position, changing how much solar radiation the Earth receives – resulting in changes in climate.

☑ **Eccentricity cycle**: the Earth's orbit changes approximately every 100 000 years. More circular orbit → warmer periods; more **elliptical** orbit → cooler periods.

☑ **Axial tilt cycle**: roughly every 40 000 years the tilt of the Earth's axis varies. Greater angle of tilt → hotter summer and colder winter.

☑ **Precession cycle**: the Earth 'wobbles' on its axis roughly every 24 000 years, changing the direction the axis is facing. This can affect the differences between seasons.

Other natural causes of climate change

Solar radiation levels vary. Lower solar radiation makes glacial periods more likely; higher solar radiation leads to interglacial periods.

A large-scale volcanic eruption can eject ash and dust into the atmosphere. This acts as a blanket over the Earth, blocking out solar radiation, causing temperatures to fall for a time.

Evidence of climate change

- **Historical sources**, such as diaries.
- **Ice cores** trap volcanic ash, microbes, air bubbles. These reveal information on climate when the ice formed.
- **Preserved pollen** provides evidence on warm and cold growing conditions.

Worked example

Explain **one** source of evidence used to investigate natural climate change in the past. **(4 marks)**

One possible source of evidence for natural climate change is growth rings from trees. When trees are cut scientists look at the width of the rings. Wider rings indicate a warmer, wetter climate and thinner rings indicate a colder, drier climate.

Now try this

Explain how volcanic activity can cause climate change. **(3 marks)**

Human activity

A key contributor to global warming is rising levels of greenhouse gases, which are released by human activities including industry, transport, energy production and farming.

Enhanced greenhouse effect
Human activity releases increasing levels of CO_2 and other greenhouse gases into the atmosphere, increasing the greenhouse effect – more warming.

② Much of this heat energy is radiated back into space.

③ Greenhouse gases in the atmosphere, such as CO_2, trap some of the heat.

① Heat energy from the Sun passes through the atmosphere and heats up the Earth.

Industry – rising demand for consumer goods increases production, burning more fossil fuels, which release greenhouse gases.

Energy – new technologies and population growth increase demand for electricity produced from coal, oil and natural gas, which all produce greenhouse gases.

Human causes of climate change

Farming – global population growth increases demand for food. Mechanisation burns more fuel, and the demand for meat for Western-style diets increases methane levels.

Transport – rising affluence increases car ownership and air travel, releasing more greenhouse gases into the atmosphere.

Negative impacts of climate change on the environment

- Melting ice sheets and retreating glaciers add water to oceans, making sea levels rise. Arctic melting could cause the Gulf Stream to move further south, leading to **colder temperatures** in Western Europe.
- Rising sea levels will cause **coastal flooding**. Soils will become contaminated with salt, causing plants to die.

Negative impacts of climate change on people

- Changes in climates near the Equator, such as Africa's Sahel, could mean longer periods of less rainfall, so **lower crop yields**.
- Many low-lying islands like the Maldives face **greater flood risk from rising sea levels**. There will be more coastal flooding, loss of beaches and loss of coral reefs. Some islands will have to be evacuated.

Worked example

Suggest **one** negative impact of climate change on the environment.   **(2 marks)**

Climate change means that glaciers are melting rapidly. This means that river systems and ecosystems that depend on spring glacier melt will be flooded in the short term and have too little water in the long term.

Worked example

Suggest **one** negative impact of climate change on people.   **(2 marks)**

One negative impact of climate change is the reduction in crop yields in countries like Tanzania because of longer periods of drought. This could lead to food shortages.

 It is important to read the question carefully – as these two similar questions show!

Now try this

Explain how **two** human activities are contributing to climate change.   **(4 marks)**

The UK's climate

The UK has a distinct climate, which has changed over the last 1000 years and which varies from region to region.

Past climate changes

Our climate has been very different in the past.

- During the **Medieval Warm Period** (950–1100) higher temperatures meant greater crop yields and a growing population. This was due to increased **solar radiation**.
- During the **Little Ice Age** (1600–1685) temperatures were low enough to freeze the Thames, due to increased **volcanic activity** and decreased solar radiation.

The UK's climate today

Today the UK has a **temperate**, wet climate. Extreme weather is rare, but the meeting of major air masses makes **frontal rainfall** common.

North-west Britain: mild winters, cool summers

North-east Britain: cold winters, cool summers

South-west Britain: mild winters, warm summers

South-east Britain: cold winters, warm summers

Impact of the UK's location

The UK is located between 50° N and 60° N. This and other factors have an impact on climate.

1 **Maritime influence**: most of the air reaching the UK contains lots of moisture, as we are surrounded by sea, leading to rainfall all year.

2 **Prevailing wind**: the main or prevailing wind for the UK comes from the south-west. This air travels long distances over the Atlantic Ocean, bringing moisture, leading to more rainfall.

3 **North Atlantic Drift**: this ocean current brings warm water north to the UK. In the winter this makes the UK climate milder than would be expected for its latitude.

4 **Atmospheric circulation**: the UK is near the 'boundary' between the northern Ferrel and Polar circulation cells. This is where warmer air from the south and cooler air from the north meet, causing unsettled weather.

5 **Altitude**: the higher an area is, the cooler and wetter it is, so areas in the UK vary.

There are significant regional variations within the UK, due to different combinations of the factors listed above.

Worked example

Study the climate graph of the UK.

1 Which month experienced the lowest amount of precipitation? **(1 mark)**

September

2 What was the difference between the maximum and minimum temperatures in July? **(1 mark)**

10 °C

Make sure you read graphs accurately. Use a ruler!

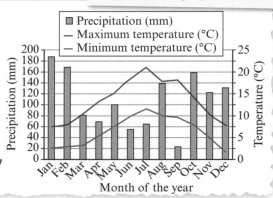

UK climate graph 2014

- Precipitation (mm)
- Maximum temperature (°C)
- Minimum temperature (°C)

Month of the year

Now try this

Explain how the North Atlantic Drift affects the climate of the UK. **(2 marks)**

Tropical cyclones

Tropical cyclones are also known as hurricanes and typhoons. You need to know how, where and when they occur, and their key characteristics.

How tropical cyclones form

Tropical cyclones need a source of warm, moist air and warm ocean temperatures (27°C plus).

1 Rising warm air causes thunderstorms, which group together, making a strong flow.

2 An area of very low pressure forms at the centre of the converged storms.

3 The storms rotate, accelerating in and up, forming a tropical cyclone.

Tropical cyclones form in tropical areas where a rotation force, created by the **Coriolis effect**, forms part of the global circulation of the atmosphere. The rotation is due to deflection of winds moving north and south of the Equator.

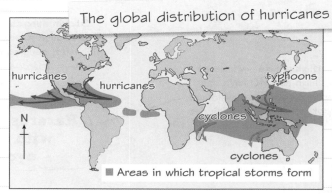

The global distribution of hurricanes

hurricanes hurricanes typhoons cyclones cyclones

■ Areas in which tropical storms form

Tropical cyclone characteristics

☑ Very low pressure

☑ Form a cylinder of rising, spiralling air surrounding an **eye** of descending, high-pressure air

☑ Cloud banks called the **eye wall** surround the eye

☑ Often 400 km wide and 10 km high

Frequency of tropical cyclones

Tropical cyclones are more likely to happen:

☑ June–November in the northern tropics

☑ November–April in the southern tropics.

They are more likely to happen in cooler years, but numbers are hard to predict.

Remember that any exam question can involve using your geographical skills as well as testing your geography knowledge and understanding.

Tropical cyclone movement

☑ Cyclone movement is determined by the prevailing winds and ocean currents.

☑ The cyclone's **track** is influenced by how far it travels over the ocean: it will collect more moisture, increasing its strength.

☑ Tropical cyclones can travel 600 km a day at 40 km/h.

☑ Cyclone movement can be forecast using satellite images.

Worked example

The chart shows tropical cyclone tracks in the North Atlantic for July–September 2014.

Using the chart, give the approximate latitude and longitude of the source of tropical cyclone Bertha. **(1 mark)**

12°N, 54°W

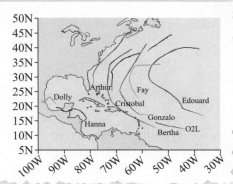

Now try this

State **one** factor that is needed for tropical cyclones to form.

(1 mark)

Tropical cyclone hazards

Tropical cyclones are natural weather hazards in themselves, and also because of the hazardous effects they produce.

Storm surges – tropical cyclones can cause a large mass of water to hit land, causing damage to beaches and coastal habitats.

High winds – winds as high as 240 km/h can uproot trees and buildings, potentially causing injuries and loss of life.

Landslides – intense rainfall causes the soil to be saturated and become heavy. This saturated soil then slides downhill.

Hazards associated with tropical cyclones

Intense rainfall – heavy persistent rainfall can lead to flooding, damaging property and leaving people stranded.

Coastal flooding – damage to property and lives is increased due to flooding.

The Saffir–Simpson scale

The Saffir-Simpson scale classifies tropical cyclones into five categories.

Category	Wind speed (km/hour)	Storm surge (metres)	Damage
1	119–153	1.0–1.7	Some damage – trees lose branches, power lines brought down
2	154–177	1.8–2.6	Roofs and windows damaged, some trees blown over, coastal flooding
3	178–208	2.7–3.8	Structural damage to buildings. Flooding over 1 m up to 10 km inland
4	209–251	3.9–5.6	Major devastation – destroys buildings, floods up to 10 km inland
5	252 or higher	>5.7	Catastrophic – destruction up to 5 m above sea level. Mass evacuation needed

Worked example

The Saffir-Simpson scale is used to categorise tropical cyclones. Which of the following is the most important measurement used when deciding the category of a cyclone? **(1 mark)**

☐ **A** The length of time that the cyclone lasts
☒ **B** The wind speed in the cyclone
☐ **C** The size of the cyclone
☐ **D** The height of the storm clouds

Now try this

The maximum recorded wind speed for Typhoon Yolanda (November 2013) was 315 km/h, with average speeds of 280 km/h. What category was this tropical cyclone on the Saffir-Simpson scale? **(1 mark)**

Hurricane Sandy

 Located example

You will need to know and understand the different social, economic and environmental impacts that tropical cyclones can have on a named developed country.

Key facts: Hurricane Sandy

1 The hurricane travelled across the Caribbean Sea, affecting the island nations of Jamaica, Cuba and Haiti, before moving north to reach the USA.

2 It reached New Jersey on 29 October 2012.

3 By the time the hurricane reached land, wind speeds of 129 km/h were recorded.

4 The storm surges caused most of the damage to East Coast states.

5 The use of social media such as Twitter and photographs uploaded to Flickr helped with damage assessment.

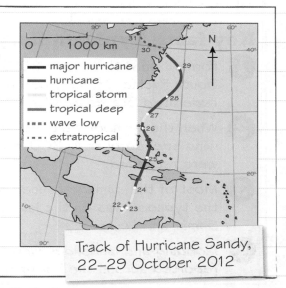

Track of Hurricane Sandy, 22–29 October 2012

Social
- Death toll of at least 150 people
- Many areas left without electricity
- Homes and businesses damaged
- Schools closed for days

What was the impact of Hurricane Sandy?

Environmental
- Storm surge caused significant damage to coastal nature reserves like the Prime Hook National Wildlife Refuge in Delaware
- Raw sewage leaked into the waters around New York and New Jersey, damaging habitats

Economic
- Estimated property damage: US$65 billion
- Government had to pay for petrol to be brought in as supplies ran out
- Income from tourism affected by cancellation of New York Marathon

Worked example

For a tropical cyclone you have studied in a named developed country, explain **two** environmental impacts. **(4 marks)**

One of the environmental impacts of Hurricane Sandy was pollution of water sources. The storm surges from the hurricane caused large-scale flooding, which resulted in raw sewage leaking into nearby water sources and damaging habitats. Another environmental impact was the damage to coastal nature reserves. For example, the storm surge caused damage to the Prime Hook National Wildlife Refuge in the state of Delaware.

Always use the located examples you were taught in class as you will have more detail for these.

What was the response to Hurricane Sandy?

Individuals: The Concert for Sandy Relief with artists such as Bon Jovi.

Organisations: The American Red Cross helped by providing relief to victims.

Government: Billions of dollars were voted through legislation to help with rebuilding and supporting victims. New York set up a new local government office to support the rebuilding.

Now try this

Evaluate the different social and economic impacts of tropical cyclones in a named developed country. **(8 marks)**

Typhoon Haiyan

🌐 **Located example**   You will need to know and understand the different social, economic and environmental impacts that tropical cyclones can have on a named emerging or developing country.

Key facts: Typhoon Haiyan

1 Formed on 2 November 2013 in the South Pacific Ocean, close to the Federated States of Micronesia.

2 When the typhoon reached land, wind speeds of over 300 km/h were recorded.

3 Most of the damage caused by the typhoon was on the islands of Samar and Leyte.

4 Flooding and landslides were reported across the Philippines.

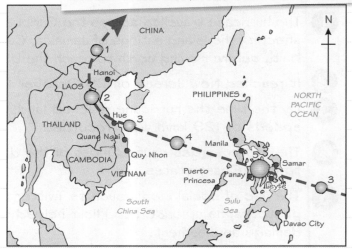

The track of Typhoon Haiyan, November 2013. The numbers show its category on the Saffir-Simpson scale

Social

- An estimated 6000 people killed and many more missing
- Significant loss of power
- An estimated 600000 people displaced from their homes
- Many homes left destroyed

What was the impact of Typhoon Haiyan?

Economic

- Estimated damage: US$2 billion
- Damage and disruption to infrastructure blocked transport across islands, making provision of aid and support difficult and expensive

Environmental

- Mangroves damaged across the islands
- Trees uprooted
- Oil spills from a tanker caused sea pollution

What was the response to Typhoon Haiyan?

Individuals: people in countries such as the UK and Canada gave money towards the relief efforts.

Organisations: the World Health Organization coordinated the international response to help the Philippine government meet the acute need for healthcare services.

Governments: in order to direct funds to help support the aftermath, the Philippines were put in a 'state of national calamity'. Aid in the form of loans and grants was provided by countries like the UK, which gave a £10 million package including emergency shelter, water and household items.

Worked example

For a tropical cyclone you have studied in a named emerging or developing country, explain **two** social impacts. **(4 marks)**

One of the social impacts of Typhoon Haiyan was the high death toll, with over 6000 people estimated killed and many more thousands missing. A second social impact was the destruction of homes, with many people left homeless.

Always use the located examples you were taught in class as you will have more detail for these.

Now try this

Evaluate the different social and environmental impacts of tropical cyclones in a named emerging or developing country. **(8 marks)**

Drought causes and locations

Drought is caused by a number of complex factors. Some places are more vulnerable to drought than others.

Arid or drought?

In **arid** areas, the normal climate is dry, because they normally have high pressure, leading to low precipitation.

The key factors in whether an area is likely to suffer from **drought** are:

- **how** it gets precipitation – at any time or in a rainy season
- **when** precipitation occurs – during winter when soil can absorb rain more easily, or in summer.

Arid environments

- Permanent low precipitation. The Sahara is arid; the Kalahari is semi-arid
- 10–250 mm precipitation a year
- High pressure conditions, no cloud cover
- Mostly located in the tropics (between 23.5°N and 23.5°S of the Equator)

Drought conditions

- Temporary low precipitation conditions
- In the UK, drought is 15 consecutive days without rainfall
- High pressure conditions, no cloud cover
- Located anywhere globally

Natural causes of drought

Meteorological

This is where an area receives less than average precipitation. In the UK, high pressure (blocking anticyclone) forces away the low pressure systems that bring rain around it. This means no rain falls over all or part of the UK for weeks.

Hydrological

This is where the hydrological cycle receives less rainfall than normal. Less precipitation means groundwater supplies and reservoirs are not refilled, leading to drought conditions.

Worked example

Explain **two** human causes of drought. **(4 marks)**

Deforestation can cause drought because trees reduce evaporation, store water and add to atmospheric moisture by transpiration.

Dam building can restrict the flow of water in the river, lowering water levels and volume, causing drought conditions further downstream.

This answer focuses on deforestation and dam building, as the question asks for only two human causes of drought. Always look carefully at the question and the number of marks available. For a question like this, remember to explain each point you make.

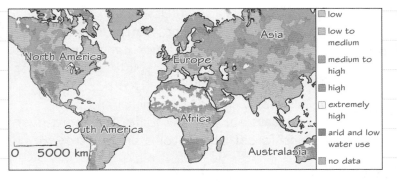

Global circulation and drought

Global circulation makes some locations more vulnerable to drought. Where the Hadley and Ferrel circulation cells are, such as Africa's Sahel, descending dry air means there is little precipitation. Rainfall occurs during a wet season; if the rains do not come, the area has drought conditions.

Now try this

Explain **one** meteorological cause of drought. **(2 marks)**

California, USA

 Located example You need to know the impacts of drought on people and ecosystems – and how individuals, organisations and governments responded – in a named developed country.

California drought, 2012 to present

In January 2014, California was experiencing its third year of drought and a state of emergency was declared. Lower than normal rainfall and snowfall on the west coast, and dependence on the over-used Colorado River, had caused water supplies to drop.

Main hazards

The main hazards in this drought were:

- ✓ **subsidence** as groundwater levels dropped, causing land to settle at a lower level
- ✓ **contamination** of land and drinking water by seawater, drawn inland by a lack of pressure
- ✓ **wildfires** which started and spread quickly, as vegetation was so dry.

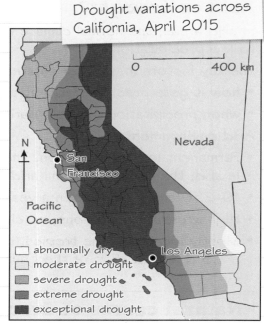

Drought variations across California, April 2015

0 — 400 km

Nevada

San Francisco

Pacific Ocean

Los Angeles

☐ abnormally dry
☐ moderate drought
☐ severe drought
☐ extreme drought
☐ exceptional drought

- Central Valley is worst affected area

- Water diverted, so wetlands and rivers get less – impacts on natural environment and wildlife, e.g. rivers too low for salmon to breed in

What are the impacts on people and ecosystems in California?

- Warm and windy weather led to wildfires – environmental damage, air pollution, destroys wildlife and habitats, risk to people's lives and property

- 542 000 acres taken out of crop production – loss of food and income

- Costing California US$2.7 billion a year – less state money to spend on services for people

- Increased extraction from groundwater/ aquifer causing subsidence – infrastructure and buildings damaged, e.g. in the San Joaquin Valley

---

How have Californians responded?

Government

- Ran public education campaigns, such as Save our Water.
- Brought in state laws requiring a 25 per cent cut in water use in California.

Organisations

- University of California research project for effectively managing groundwater.

Individuals

- Farmers encouraged to use water-efficient irrigation, such as drip irrigation.
- Homeowners encouraged to check for water leaks.
- Protestors campaigned against companies selling bottled local water.

Worked example

Suggest the impacts of drought on ecosystems in a developed country. **(3 marks)**

Much of California (USA) has been badly affected by drought. Wetlands and rivers have dried up so salmon cannot reach their breeding grounds. In dried-up forest areas, forest wildfires have become frequent, destroying animal and plant habitats and killing wildlife. Therefore river and forest ecosystems are destroyed.

Now try this

Explain **two** ways people have responded to drought in a developed country. **(4 marks)**

Ethiopia

Located example You need to know the impacts of drought on people and ecosystems – and how individuals, organisations and governments responded – in a named emerging or developing country.

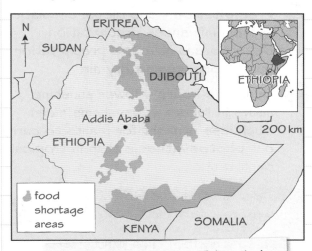

The lack of rainfall in Ethiopia in 2015 was estimated to be as severe as 1984, when global responses included Live Aid

Ethiopia, 2015

Ethiopia has suffered multiple droughts since the 1980s, when the short rainy season began to get shorter, and the long rainy season got later and less predictable. 85 per cent of the people of Ethiopia live in rural areas and rely on agriculture, so low rainfall can be devastating. The 2015 drought was the worst in 30 years.

Main hazards

The main hazards in this drought were:

- **reduction in crop yields** leading to malnutrition and death for people and livestock
- **longer journeys to find water**, taking children out of school and farmers out of fields
- **migration** in search for ways to survive, breaking up communities.

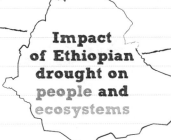

Impact of Ethiopian drought on people and ecosystems

- Death of livestock causes a food crisis
- Loss of crops means maize price rockets
- People eat less, become weak from malnutrition and more vulnerable to disease
- Girls have to walk further to get water, so cannot go to school
- Long grasses used for roofing cannot grow, so homes are unprotected

- Loss of habitat for fish and wildlife due to low water levels in reservoirs, lakes and ponds, e.g. Borkena Wetland
- Increase in disease in wild animals, because of reduced food and water supplies
- Migration of wildlife
- Loss of 200 000 hectares of forest every year due to forest fires
- Extinction of some species, e.g. Grevy zebras
- Wind and water erosion of soil

What has the response been?

Governments

- Overseas governments have given aid, e.g. the USA gave US$128.4 million in food aid for Ethiopians in 2015.

Organisations

- Aid agencies such as Oxfam and UNICEF are helping people to get water supplies.
- Education charities are trying to help people get jobs in urban areas.

Individuals

- Large charity events like Live Aid have helped raise awareness and money.

Worked example

Explain **two** impacts of drought on people living in an emerging or developing country. **(4 marks)**

Drought in Ethiopia is having significant impacts on the lives of people. For example, many of the homes are without roofs that protect them from the outside elements. This is because the lack of rainfall means many of the plants and grasses used to make roofs cannot grow. A second impact is the time spent on collecting water due to a lack of direct water supply. Many women and children are having to walk up to 20 kilometres to find water, so they have less time for farming and school.

Now try this

Suggest **one** impact of drought on ecosystems in an emerging or developing country. **(2 marks)**

The world's ecosystems

Large-scale ecosystems are found in different parts of the world and have different characteristics. Climate and local factors each play a part in where ecosystems occur.

Climate

The Earth's climate depends on energy from the Sun. It affects growing conditions for vegetation, and affects the location and characteristics of large-scale ecosystems.

1 **Temperature** – temperatures are lower at higher latitudes, so boreal forests are much colder than tropical rainforests. Growing seasons are longer in warmer locations.

2 **Precipitation** – the global circulation system influences precipitation. Desert areas have low precipitation due to descending dry air.

3 **Sunshine hours** – lower sunshine hours in tundra ecosystems mean much less sunlight for plants to carry out **photosynthesis** than in tropical rainforests.

Worked example

When describing distribution, use ODE: O = overall distribution, D = data and E = example.

Study the map showing global distribution of the world's ecosystems.

Describe the distribution of tropical forests. **(3 marks)**

The world's tropical forests are mainly found in a band stretching west to east just north and south of the Equator, between 23.50°N and S. For example, the Amazon rainforest is found mainly between the Equator and the Tropic of Capricorn in Brazil.

Boreal biome
Boreal forests are at higher latitudes where the Sun's rays are weak. Trees are adapted to the cold with needle-like leaves.

Temperate biome
Temperate forests have high rainfall and there are seasonal variations in the Sun's rays. Trees lose their leaves in the cool winters.

Tundra biome
The **tundra** is within the Arctic Circle. The Sun gives little heat here and there is little rainfall. Only tough, short grasses survive.

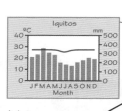

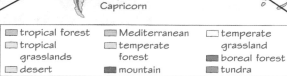

Tropical biome
Tropical rainforests are mostly found either side of the Equator. The temperature is hot and there is heavy rainfall.

	tropical forest		Mediterranean		temperate grassland
	tropical grasslands		temperate forest		boreal forest
	desert		mountain		tundra

Desert biome
Deserts are close to the Tropics of Cancer and Capricorn. This is where hot dry air sinks down to the Earth's surface and the Sun's rays are concentrated, making it very hot in the day.

Local factors

Two local factors affect the distribution of large-scale ecosystems.

1 **Rock and soil type** differences can lead to different vegetation in the same ecosystem. In NW Australia, poor, sandy soil means grasses are shorter than in other areas of tropical grassland.

2 **Altitude differences** can lead to different plants growing within the same ecosystem. The higher the altitude, the lower the temperature. At low altitudes lowland rainforests and mangroves grow; at cloud level (1 200 m), moist cloud forests occur.

Now try this

State **one** characteristic of hot deserts.

(2 marks)

Importance of the biosphere

The biosphere is important for providing resources for people (food, medicine, building materials and fuel resources) but the biosphere is being increasingly exploited.

Providing resources

natural vegetation can be replaced by crops – wheat, rice

sustainable harvests – fruit, berries, nuts

fish and meat

animal dung dried and burned

trees and shrubs

fermenting crops like sugar cane produce bioethanol

FOOD FROM THE BIOSPHERE

FUEL RESOURCES FROM THE BIOSPHERE

poppies (morphine) treat pain

How the biosphere provides resources for people

MEDICINE FROM THE BIOSPHERE

BUILDING MATERIALS FROM THE BIOSPHERE

animal dung mixed with clay and straw – bricks

aloe plant soothes skin conditions

lichens stop blood loss from cuts

straw – used for roofing and insulation

timber

Vitamin C vital – found in oranges

Commercial exploitation of the biosphere

Water	Increased water demand (urbanisation, agriculture and industry) means there is less water in the biosphere for other areas, e.g. wetlands.
Energy	Production of biofuels means that fewer food crops can be grown for local people.

Worked example

Study the satellite image of the Athabasca Oil Sands Project mine in the boreal ecosystem, Canada. Suggest the impacts this mining might have on biosphere services for local people. **(4 marks)**

The mine is extensive, around 20 km². A large area has been disturbed, destroying plants and animals that may provide food, fuel, building materials and medicines for local people.

Because the mine is extracting oil, there is a high risk of water pollution. Drinking water is a vital biosphere resource and water pollution could have a very negative impact on, for example, the health of local people.

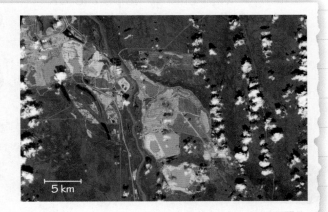

5 km

 Use the scale on the satellite image to make your answer precise.

Now try this

State **two** resources provided by the biosphere. **(2 marks)**

43

The UK's main ecosystems

The UK has its own range of varied and important ecosystems – moorlands, heaths, woodlands and wetlands, as well as marine ecosystems.

Terrestrial ecosystems

Moorlands

- Approximately 350 000 hectares of heather moorland in England and Wales
- Largest area in Scotland
- Found in upland areas
- Peat bogs and rough grassland

Heathlands

- Approximately 95 000 hectares of heathland
- Located in lowland areas of UK
- Some sites marshy, some places dry and sandy

Woodlands

- Remaining ancient woodland – Scots pine, juniper, aspen, rowan, birch and oak
- Oak woodlands like Taynish National Nature Reserve, Argyll are rich in plants and wildlife

Wetlands

- Main areas located in Scotland and East Anglia
- Waterlogged soils low in nutrients

Marine ecosystems

Marine ecosystems are important to the UK.

- **Tourism**: an estimated 250 million people visit the UK's coastline each year, generating income for the local economy and providing employment.
- **Energy**: wind energy helps the UK reduce reliance on fossil fuels and meet carbon targets. The London Array is the world's largest offshore wind farm – 175 turbines.
- **Fishing**: marine ecosystems provide jobs in commercial fishing.

How marine ecosystems are degraded

1. The development of coastlines can lead to destruction of plant and wildlife habitats, e.g. salt marshes.

2. Climate change allows new species to move into new areas, which may alter the food web.

3. Overfishing of fish species (like cod in the North Sea) impacts the wider ecosystem and damages the food chain.

4. Fertilisers used by farmers can lead to **eutrophication** from chemicals reaching the sea.

Remember – a marine ecosystem is a community of organisms (e.g. fish) interacting with each other and their environment.

Worked example

Suggest **one** way humans can damage marine ecosystems. **(2 marks)**

One way humans can damage marine ecosystems is by overfishing fish species such as cod. This disrupts the food chain as cod eat smaller fish, which then increase in number.

Now try this

Explain why marine ecosystems are important to the UK as a resource. **(4 marks)**

Tropical rainforest features

Tropical rainforest (TRF) is vital to the world's other ecosystems – and to humans. Tropical rainforest has distinctive characteristics and high levels of biodiversity.

Components

The tropical rainforest is a very productive ecosystem. It has:

✓ **biotic** components – living parts of the ecosystem (plants, animals, humans)

✓ **abiotic** components – non-living parts of the ecosystem (climate, soil, water).

Biotic and abiotic components depend on each other. Their interaction makes the ecosystem function.

Indigenous tribes hunt animals for food, carry out small-scale farming and spread seeds of plants when eating fruit and nuts.

The soils are low in nutrients because of **leaching**. Heavy rainfall seeps into the soil, and takes nutrients and minerals with it as it moves downwards.

Chemical weathering is common in the bedrock in TRF because of warm, moist conditions, but nutrients are not available for plant growth.

Another biotic characteristic is nutrient recycling, as you can see in the Gersmehl model (below).

Worked example

Study the climate graph opposite for the Amazon tropical rainforest.

Complete the bar graph (precipitation in mm) using data from the table. **(2 marks)**

Month	Precipitation (mm)
June	110
July	75

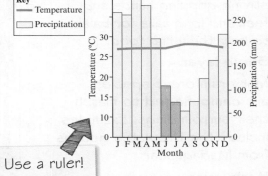

Be accurate. Use a ruler!

Gersmehl model

Nutrients are transferred between three key stores: biomass, litter and soil.

Biomass is the largest store – nutrients are recycled quickly because of year-round plant growth and rapid decomposition of dead matter due to warm, wet conditions.

Therefore the **soil** and **litter** are small nutrient stores.

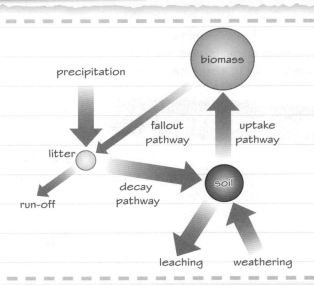

Now try this

Compare biotic components and abiotic components of the tropical rainforest. **(3 marks)**

45

TRF biodiversity and adaptations

The tropical rainforest is high in both biodiversity and productivity. The diverse range of plants and animals has cleverly adapted to these unique conditions.

High biodiversity

✓ The tropical rainforest is the most productive large-scale ecosystem on Earth.

✓ TRF is believed to be the oldest ecosystem, so species have been evolving for a long time.

✓ It has a complex layered structure, creating a range of wildlife habitats.

✓ There is a hot, wet climate all year, with no seasons.

✓ Long hours of sunlight and warm temperatures are excellent for photosynthesis.

Animal adaptations

Main canopy

Leaves, fruit, berries, nuts and flowers are mainly 30–40 m up. Monkeys have evolved strong gripping hands and feet and long tails for balance to help them find food.

Shrub layer

Many rainforest species are **camouflaged** to match their surroundings. Examples include the Uroplatus geckos from Madagascar.

Herb layer

Only 2 per cent of sunlight reaches here. Animals have evolved camouflage to help them hide in the shadows.

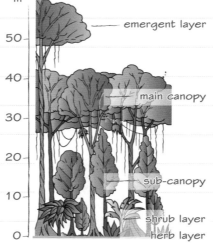

Plant adaptations

Emergent trees have adapted by growing up to 40 m to reach above the canopy, to get more light for photosynthesis.

Trees in the TRF are **deciduous**, losing their leaves in drier periods to help conserve water.

Lianas (plants) climb tree trunks to reach light.

Plants have evolved thick, waxy leaves with **drip-tips** so water runs off them, to stop mould growing and prevent the leaves from rotting.

Nutrients are only in the top layer of soil, so tree roots must be shallow. **Buttress roots** have developed to provide stability.

Worked example

Study the photograph of a tree in a tropical rainforest.
Describe the adaptation shown in the photograph.   **(2 marks)**

The adaptation shown in the photograph is buttress roots, which help to support the tree.

This is a good answer as it focuses on one important adaptation.

Now try this

Suggest **one** reason why tropical rainforests have high levels of biodiversity.   **(2 marks)**

TRF goods and services

The tropical rainforest (TRF) is vital for human life, providing a range of goods and services including food, medicines, timber and recreation. However, this is under threat from climate change.

GOODS

Source of food like fruits and nuts for indigenous tribes

Diverse range of plant species – key ingredients in drugs

Tropical rainforest goods and services

SERVICES

Acts as a carbon store – taking in up to 2 billion tonnes of CO_2 every year

Source of revenue, with the tropical rainforests a popular tourist attraction

Timber for manufacturing furniture, for construction and for fuel

Home to many indigenous tribes

Effects of climate change

Scientists believe climate change will affect different aspects of the TRF.

- **Structure**: long periods of drier conditions slow down the process of decomposition, reducing the biomass store.

- **Functioning**: longer periods of drier conditions could stop 'cloud functioning'. This process provides water for the ecosystem.

- **Biodiversity**: changes in climatic conditions (e.g. less rainfall) threaten the survival of plant and animal species, leading to invasion of non-TRF species more tolerant to the changing conditions.

Worked example

Suggest **two** ways climate change presents a threat to tropical rainforests. **(4 marks)**

One way climate change presents a threat to the tropical rainforest is through the impact on plant and animal species. Drier conditions could kill off particular species and bring in new species, changing the balance of the ecosystem. Secondly, climate change could prevent 'cloud functioning' from occurring, reducing the water available for the functioning of the ecosystem.

An alternative answer could be about the impact of climate change on the structure of the TRF.

Now try this

State **one** example of a service provided by tropical rainforests. **(1 mark)**

Deforestation in tropical rainforests

Deforestation of tropical rainforest has both economic and social causes.

Causes of TRF deforestation

The main reasons for clearing rainforest are resource extraction, conversion to agriculture and population pressure.

Road building – to transport resources like iron ore and timber; often built without proper controls

Mining – rising demand and rising prices for minerals in rainforest (e.g. Carajas iron ore mine, Brazil)

Rapid population growth – rising demand for housing and agriculture. Madagascar population 4 million in 1950; 20.7 million in 2010

Oil palm plantations – in demand as ingredient in foods and cosmetics, and as biofuel

Subsistence agriculture – land cleared to grow crops quickly loses its nutrients, so farmers clear more

Illegal logging – high demand for timber in the Western world

Cattle ranching – needs vast areas of land; biggest cause of deforestation in the Amazon

7.3 million hectares of rainforest are cleared each year: the equivalent of 36 football pitches of forest every minute.

Worked example

Study the photograph of a palm oil plantation in the Indonesian rainforest.

Explain how clearing land for agricultural use such as oil palm plantations is causing deforestation in tropical rainforests.

(3 marks)

Tropical rainforests are being cleared to make room for cattle ranching because of increasing demands for beef. Other agricultural uses include large-scale oil palm plantations. There is a high demand for palm oil as it is used in food products and cosmetics, and as biofuel. Farmers can make a lot of money by clearing forest and planting oil palm plantations.

Indonesia's oil palm plantations cover 9 million hectares; 26 million hectares are projected for 2025.

Now try this

Explain why resource extraction is causing the deforestation of tropical rainforests. **(4 marks)**

Tropical rainforest management

 Located example You need to know how political and economic factors have contributed towards the sustainable management of a rainforest in a named region.

Amazon rainforest

The Amazon rainforest is an important ecosystem that needs sustainable management.

✓ It consists of one-third of the planet's remaining tropical rainforest.

✓ It provides resources for people locally and worldwide, including food, water, timber and medicines.

✓ It is home to a diverse range of plants and animals, with over 1300 bird and 40000 plant species.

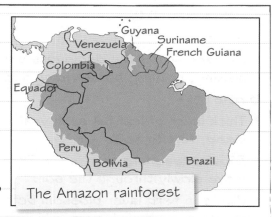

The Amazon rainforest

Sustainable management

Government policies (governance) – Brazil

- National Forests belong to the state, but government can grant timber companies concessions to manage certain areas.

- 31 National Forests covering 16 million hectares – an area larger than England!

- Biodiversity survey must be carried out before logging, to establish which areas need protection.

Commodity value

- In parts of the Amazon (e.g. Paragominas) timber firms are realising that undamaged forest is a commercial asset and can yield sustainable income.

- 'Sustainable management' or 'reduced-impact logging' (RIL) can be more profitable than 'clear all' methods of timber extraction.

- RIL is up to 12 per cent cheaper than conventional logging.

For a named tropical rainforest, explain **two** ways ecotourism is helping to manage the tropical rainforest more sustainably.

(4 marks)

One way ecotourism is helping to manage the Amazon tropical rainforest in Brazil is through the construction of visitor centres. These are used to help educate local people and tourists about the importance of conserving the local area. Secondly, ecotourism is providing an alternative form of employment for local people that doesn't involve removing trees: for example, by creating jobs as guides.

Make sure you **name** an area and **explain**, not just describe, the impacts of ecotourism.

Conventional logging

👎 The TRF is fragmented and species become endangered.

👎 For every tree cut down, 10–20 others are damaged.

Reduced-impact logging

👍 Selected mature trees cut down.

👍 'Seed' trees are left to help quicker regrowth.

👍 Direction of falling trees calculated to reduce damage to other trees.

👍 Less fragmentation and quicker regeneration.

Now try this

Explain **one** reason why tropical rainforests require sustainable management.

(2 marks)

Deciduous woodlands features

Deciduous woodlands are mainly found in Europe, south-east USA, China and Japan. Like TRF, deciduous woodland has **abiotic** and **biotic** components, with distinct characteristics.

Components

Abiotic

* **Humans** shape the deciduous woodland by walking, cycling, horse-riding and picnics.

Biotic

* Thick layer of leaf fall each year creates **deep, fertile soil**.
* **Slower leaching** than in the TRF – nutrients move slowly through the soil.
* Plants in herb layer blossom before larger plants grow their leaves, which block sunlight.
* Bogs and ponds provide habitats for a range of plant and animal species.

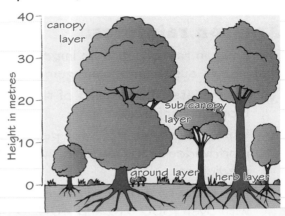

The deciduous woodland ecosystem has four layers: canopy layer, sub-canopy layer, herb layer and ground layer.

Worked example

Study the climate graphs for a deciduous woodland ecosystem (opposite) and a tropical rainforest ecosystem (see page 45). Compare the differences in climatic conditions. **(3 marks)**

Overall on average the tropical rainforest ecosystem experiences high temperatures throughout the year, around 27–29 °C, whereas in the deciduous woodland ecosystem there is a greater range, and a maximum average temperature of only 17 °C. Tropical rainforests receive much more rainfall overall, with most falling between December and May, whereas deciduous woodlands receive less rainfall throughout the year, but have most rainfall from October to February.

Make sure you compare both the temperature and the precipitation.

Gersmehl model

In deciduous woodlands the biomass and soils stores are a similar size.

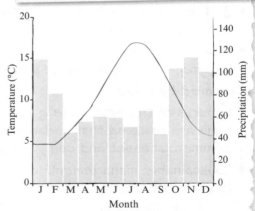

L = litter store   B = biomass store   S = soil

Look back at page 45 and compare this model with the one for TRF. Remember that the size of the circles indicates the proportion of nutrients stored, and the width of the arrows indicates the amount of nutrients moved between stores.

Now try this

State **one** characteristic of deciduous woodlands. **(1 mark)**

Deciduous woodlands adaptations

You will need to know why deciduous woodlands have moderate levels of biodiversity and how plants and animals have adapted to the ecosystem.

Moderate biodiversity

Deciduous woodlands have fewer types of species compared to TRFs because of:

- **lower food production** levels in the winter
- **smaller size** ecosystem than TRF, so less space for plant and animal species
- **higher latitude** = lower temperatures and fewer sunlight hours: not as efficient for photosynthesis or food production for animals.

However, some characteristics support biodiversity.

- Deciduous woodlands have rainfall all year with four distinct seasons – spring, summer, autumn and winter – which leads to different adaptations by species.
- The ecosystem's four layers (see page 50) create a range of wildlife habitats.

Animal adaptation

Animals in deciduous woodlands have to adapt to the harsh winters.

Birds **migrate** away from the UK to warmer conditions.

Squirrels **store food**, burying it in spring and summer to use in winter.

Some animals such as hedgehogs **hibernate** in winter.

Plant adaptation

Deciduous trees drop leaves in the autumn to reduce transpiration and **conserve** water during cold winter conditions.

Trees **spread their branches** wide for greater access to sunlight.

Plants have evolved **broad, thin leaves** to absorb maximum sunlight in the summer.

Deciduous trees have **large, deep root systems** for stability and to reach nutrients and groundwater.

Worked example

Study the picture of an oak tree. Explain **two** ways deciduous trees such as oaks are adapted to their environment.   **(4 marks)**

Oak trees have adapted to survive in the deciduous woodlands ecosystem by having a strong, deep root system. This means that during periods of more extreme windy weather the tree has more stability. A second way oak trees have adapted to the ecosystem is by dropping their leaves in autumn, which helps reduce the rate of transpiration and conserves water.

Look at the photo for clues!

Now try this

Suggest **one** way animals living in deciduous woodlands are adapted to their environment.   **(2 marks)**

Deciduous woodlands goods and services

Deciduous woodlands provide a range of goods and services including timber, fuel, conservation and recreation. However, the ecosystem is under threat from climate change.

GOODS

Wood used for fuel in wood-burning stoves

Wood pellets used in power stations to burn biomass

Wood pellets – the most common biomass fuel for power stations

Contribute to 13 million tonnes of timber used each year in UK construction

Deciduous woodland goods and services

SERVICES

Act as carbon store – UK woodlands take in 1 million tonnes of carbon per year

Protect rare plant and animal species

Rare native bluebells need deciduous woodlands

Regularly used for cycling, walking and horse-riding

Oak is a useful wood for construction

Walking is a popular pastime in the New Forest

Climate change

Scientists believe climate change could have an impact on deciduous woodlands.

- **Structure**: rising temperatures and drier conditions **increase the risk of forest fires**, which could cause significant damage to plants and animal habitats.

- **Functioning**: increased periods of drought could **threaten the survival of deciduous woodland trees** because they become more vulnerable to diseases.

- **Biodiversity**: milder winters could mean pests could survive in warmer conditions, causing a **rise in diseases** that could put vulnerable species in danger.

Worked example

Describe **one** service provided by deciduous woodlands. **(2 marks)**

Deciduous woodlands provide a service in the form of a range of recreational activities for people. For example, many people like to use the woodlands for days out walking with the family and horse-riding.

Always read the question carefully – here only one service needs to be described.

Now try this

Explain how climate change presents a threat to deciduous woodlands. **(4 marks)**

Deforestation in deciduous woodlands

There are economic and political causes behind the deforestation of deciduous woodlands.

Causes of deciduous woodland deforestation

The main reasons for clearing deciduous woodlands are urbanisation and population growth, timber extraction and agricultural change.

Replanting with conifers – 38 per cent of deciduous woodland cleared in 20th century

Conifers more economic
- faster growing
- easier to manage
- quicker return

Cost of conifer plantations
- dense canopy blocks light
- monoculture – less variety
- non-native species
- reduces biodiversity

Pesticide damage – woods often border farmland, so chemicals sprayed on crops can damage trees and other wildlife

Need for farmland – most land cleared centuries ago, so rising demand affects ancient woodlands

Higher car ownership – demand for wider roads to ease congestion

Land to build new homes – pressure on green belt sites where houses can fetch higher prices

A lot of deciduous woodland is not protected by law, so it is increasingly at risk of being cleared for new development.

Worked example

Study the photograph of a coniferous forest in the UK.
Explain **one** reason deciduous woodlands have been replaced with coniferous forests. **(2 marks)**

Coniferous trees grow faster, so timber can be extracted and money generated in a shorter timescale than timber from deciduous woodlands.

You do not need a long answer here – you are only asked to explain one point.

Now try this

This question is looking for two clear causes of deforestation. You should identify each cause and then explain how this is leading to the removal of deciduous woodlands.

Explain **two** causes of deforestation in deciduous woodlands. **(4 marks)**

Deciduous woodlands management

 Located example You need to know about different approaches to the sustainable use and management of deciduous woodlands in a named region.

The New Forest

The New Forest is a National Park, which requires sustainable management for a number of reasons.

1 The National Park is a popular tourist attraction, with over 15 million visitors each year contributing towards the local economy.

2 The movement of visitors through the forest is increasing litter, causing erosion of paths and increasing air pollution from traffic.

3 Softwood and hardwood timber is being extracted for commercial use.

4 40 per cent of the woodland is privately owned, and is often left unmanaged.

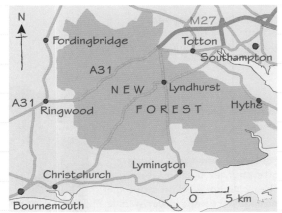

New trees planted to replace those cut down

The Green Leaf Tourism Scheme promotes use of local products; businesses give percentage of land for wildlife and encourage visitors to walk or use bikes

Careful management by National Park Authority (NPA), with dedicated walking and cycling routes in more fragile areas

Tree felling controlled – some trees left; older trees felled and left to rot on forest floor

Sustainable management of New Forest

Awareness raising by NPA – leaflets, posters – on importance of sustainability in the New Forest

Work restricted between April and August minimises disturbance to nesting birds

Landowners funded to plant native tree species by NPA

Pesticide use limited to prevent damage to the natural ecosystem

Sustainable transport schemes for tourists (e.g. bike and electric vehicle hire) helping to reduce congestion and air pollution

Worked example

Using a named example, explain **two** ways in which a deciduous woodland is being sustainably managed. **(4 marks)**

One of the ways the New Forest National Park is being managed is through the careful removal of trees. When trees are felled they are replaced with new trees and the work is restricted between the months of April and August to avoid disturbing nesting birds.

A second strategy used in the New Forest is the introduction of more environmentally friendly transport. Visitors to the National Park are encouraged to hire bikes and follow bike routes which do not cross environmentally fragile areas.

Now try this

Turn to page 49 for more about tropical rainforests.

Assess the following statement: 'Sustainable management of tropical rainforests and deciduous woodlands is vital for their future existence.' **(8 marks + 4 marks for SPGST)**

Paper 1

Paper 1 focuses on the physical environment, and has three sections: A, B and C. Each section has a range of different types of question, including an 8-mark extended writing question.

Paper 1 has three sections:

- **A: The changing landscape of the UK**
- **B: Weather hazards and climate change**
- **C: Ecosystems, biodiversity and management**

There will be one 8-mark extended writing question per section.

In **Section A** you only need to answer on two of: Coastal landscapes, River landscapes, Glaciated landscapes.

SPGST

The extended writing question for **Section C** will be worth **8 marks + 4 marks for SPGST = 12 marks** in total.

With SPGST, the best answers will:

- ✓ use accurate **spelling** and **punctuation**
- ✓ follow the rules of **grammar**
- ✓ use a wide range of **specialist terms** appropriately.

Command words

In Paper 1, the command words for the extended question could be 'assess', 'evaluate' or 'examine'.

Assess and **evaluate** questions can draw on a resource, but don't always.

- Without a resource, they test Assessment Objectives 2 (4 marks) and 3 (4 marks).
- With a resource, they test Assessment Objectives 3 (4 marks) and 4 (4 marks).

With an **assess** question, you need to:

- weigh all the factors up against each other
- decide which are the most important.

With an **evaluate** question, you need to:

- review all the information
- bring it together to form a supported judgement in your conclusion.

Examine questions:

- always draw on a **resource**, e.g. a map or a photo
- test Assessment Objectives 3 (4 marks) and 4 (4 marks).

With an **examine** question, you need to:

- break things down into individual elements
- explain how each element links to the question
- explain how the different elements link together.

Assessment Objectives

For **Assessment Objective 2 (AO2)** you have to show you understand geographical concepts and relationships. For a good answer, you need to:

- show that you understand the concepts involved in the question
- show that you know how processes, places and the environment are linked.

For **Assessment Objective 3 (AO3)** you need to apply what you know. For a good answer, you need to:

- use your knowledge to interpret, analyse and evaluate – and then make judgements
- support your judgements with evidence such as strengths, weaknesses, alternatives and data.

For **Assessment Objective 4 (AO4)** you must use your skills to investigate and communicate well. For a good answer, you need to:

- choose the right skill or technique to investigate the question **and** to communicate your findings
- put together a clear, well-balanced answer.

Now try this

Structure your answer with an introduction, middle and conclusion. Check your work for SPGST.

Write a plan for your answer to this question.

Assess the following statement: 'Different approaches are needed to ensure the successful sustainable management of deciduous woodlands.'   **(8 marks + 4 marks for SPGST)**

An urban world

Over the last 50 years urbanisation has occurred at different rates and in different ways in developed, emerging and developing countries – with different effects.

Global trends

More than half the world's population now lives in towns and cities as a result of **urbanisation**. Current trends predict that the urban population could rise to 5 billion by 2030.

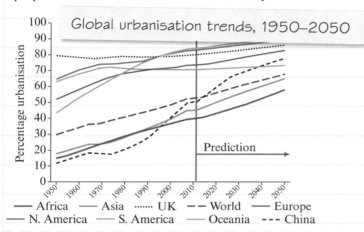

Global urbanisation trends, 1950–2050

Legend: — Africa — Asia ······ UK – – World — Europe — N. America — S. America — Oceania – – – China

Variations

In **developed countries**, the main cause of urbanisation is **industrialisation**.

✓ For example, in the UK in the 18th/19th centuries the mechanisation of farming and rise of factory jobs meant people moved from rural areas to cities.

In **emerging** and **developing countries**, recent rapid urbanisation has been caused by:

✓ **rural to urban migration** – people moving from rural areas for a better quality of life

✓ **natural increase** – birth rates in these countries are higher than death rates.

Effects

As urbanisation increases and cities grow:

- in developing countries, illegal, unplanned **shanty towns** often develop
- air, noise and water pollution all increase
- gap between rich and poor widens – often more in emerging and developing countries
- investment increases, leading to greater economic opportunities.

Worked example

Study the graph (opposite) of some of the world's largest cities.

1 Calculate the difference between the populations of Tokyo and Mexico City. **(1 mark)**

17 million

2 Explain **one** effect of rapid urbanisation in emerging countries like Brazil. **(2 marks)**

One of the effects of rapid urbanisation in Brazil is the increase in illegal and unplanned shanty towns. These develop because there is not enough permanent housing for people migrating to urban areas.

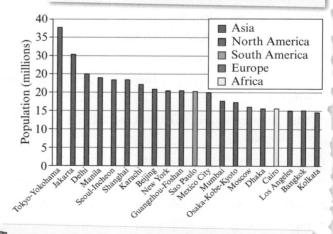

The world's 20 largest cities, 2015

Legend: Asia, North America, South America, Europe, Africa

Make sure you explain, not just describe.

Now try this

Explain **one** factor that has caused variations in urbanisation rates between emerging and developed countries.

(2 marks)

UK urbanisation differences

A range of factors has caused the rate and degree of urbanisation to vary between different regions and centres in the UK.

This choropleth map shows population density in the UK. The darker the colour, the denser the population.

Population distribution is uneven, but is generally lower in the north and higher in the south.

The overall population density of the UK is 266 people/km².

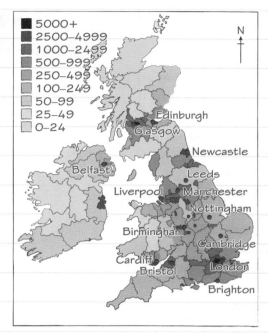

Dots show the major urban centres in the UK.

Major urban centres have the highest population density.

London has the highest population density in the UK, with over 5000 people/km².

In the major cities of London, Liverpool and Portsmouth the population density is over 3000 people/km².

Why population density varies

- In the north, the population density tends to be lower because there are fewer major cities and the high relief of the land makes it more difficult to build settlements.

- The population density may also be lower in certain parts of the UK because of the climate. In Scotland, the cooler climate makes living in the area more difficult due to more extreme weather conditions.

- One of the reasons for the higher urban populations in the UK is the location of ports. For example, Liverpool is a densely populated city because of its port, which provides opportunities for industry and employment.

Worked example

Explain **two** factors that cause differences in the rate of urbanisation between different UK regions. **(4 marks)**

One factor that causes the rate of urbanisation to be different between UK regions is whether an area specialises in a particular type of manufacturing or not. This happened a lot in the Industrial Revolution. For example, Birmingham developed a specialism in brass production. This boosted wealth and employment in the area, and people moved in from other areas to live near the factories.

Another factor that has caused different rates of urbanisation in different areas is whether there have been improvements in transport in the area or not. When one place gets better road and rail connections, this increased connectivity attracts people to live there, rather than in less connected centres.

You need to make two points, then explain **why** for each point.

Now try this

Study the choropleth map of population density above.
Describe the relationship between population distribution and the UK's main urban centres. **(3 marks)**

Context and structure

 Case study You will need to know the site, situation, connectivity and structure of a named city in the UK. Here we look at Birmingham as an example.

Birmingham

Site – located on Birmingham plateau in a prime part of the Midlands region; began as a small village, built on a dry point site, south-facing sandstone ridge.

Situation – located centrally in England, Birmingham has excellent road links to the north and south.

Connectivity – a range of transport networks connecting the city at different scales: Birmingham International Airport, Birmingham New Street railway station, easy access to M5, M6, M6 toll and M42, providing national links to the West Midlands.

Cultural – a multicultural city with an estimated 22 per cent of the population born outside the UK. In the 2011 Census, 13.5 per cent defined themselves as Pakistani and 6 per cent as Indian.

Environmental – Birmingham is one of the leading cities for parks, with an estimated 571 parks covering 3500 hectares. In 2010, the city was ranked 15th for sustainable cities in the UK.

Worked example

For a named UK city, explain the function and land use of the CBD.   **(4 marks)**

The CBD or Central Business District in Birmingham is the main financial centre of the city, with the local government offices also situated here. The land use is a combination of offices, shops, restaurants, apartments and hotels.

Birmingham has recently undergone redevelopment with new shopping centres, like the Bullring and Grand Central. The CBD is the most accessible part of the city, with key transport links to it, like the M6 motorway to the rest of the West Midlands.

You could be asked to talk about any aspect of your UK city structure. Make sure you understand the function and land use of the CBD, inner city, suburbs and urban–rural fringe.

City structure

CBD	Inner city	Suburbs	Urban–rural fringe
Main hub of city with offices, shops, theatres and hotels. Redevelopment has introduced new buildings recently, e.g. Bullring Shopping Centre.	Redeveloped in 1970s. Tightly packed terraces and blocks of flats.	Built during the 1930s, 1950s and 1960s. Building density is much lower, mainly semi-detached housing.	Fewer, larger, more recently built detached houses. Out-of-town shopping centres and industrial units also sited here.

Birmingham's CBD

Terrace in Sparkbrook

Edgbaston

New estate

Now try this

Explain the **site** and **situation** of a major UK city.   **(3 marks)**

A changing UK city

 Case study You will need to know how a named UK city is being changed by movements of people, employment and services.

Processes that change a city

Urbanisation
- influenced by manufacturing, e.g. jewellery
- small housing built for workers coming in from countryside, e.g. Small Heath

Suburbanisation
- 1920s rising population meant building new housing on outskirts of city
- new estates, mainly semi-detached houses

Counter-urbanisation
- five new comprehensive development areas built in inner city
- people forced out of urban areas to places like Redditch

Re-urbanisation
- more people want to live in centre again, close to work/amenities
- modernisation of flats and building of new apartments near canal

National migration

In Birmingham, the main causes are:
- **people moving out** to retirement destinations in the south, such as Bournemouth
- **people moving in** because increased investment in Birmingham's CBD has created more employment opportunities.

International migration

In Birmingham, the main causes are:
- **people moving in currently** who have fled conflict in countries such as Syria
- **people moving in in the past** in response to employee shortages, encouraged by the UK government to fill key job posts.

Impacts of migration

1 **Younger population**: with migrants settling in Birmingham, the percentage of people aged 20–35 is higher than the UK average – 66 per cent of the population is under 45.

2 **Multiculturalism**: 42 per cent of residents are from ethnic groups other than white; 16 per cent do not have English as a main language.

3 **Ethnic communities**: in the 1970s many migrants settled in Sparkbrook and Sparkhill (cheaper housing). Communities have developed with their own shops, places of worship.

4 **Housing**: in 2015, it was estimated that the city's housing demands were higher than expected, rising by an extra 5000.

5 **Services**: having more people in the city is putting increased pressure on key services, such as GP surgeries.

Worked example

Describe the population pyramid for the city of Birmingham. **(3 marks)**

The population pyramid shows a higher than UK average for the age groups from 0 to 34. The highest age group is 20–24, with an approximate total population of 98 000.

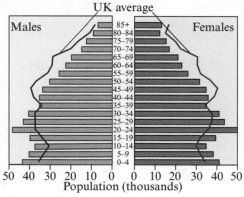

Now try this

Explain how international migration can impact on cities. **(4 marks)**

Globalisation and economic change

 Case study You will need to know the causes of deindustrialisaton (the decline of industries in an area) and the impacts this has had on a named UK city.

Population characteristics of Birmingham

- In 2014, Birmingham had a total population of approximately 1.1 million people – an increase of 9.9 per cent since 2004.

- Birmingham has a youthful population. In 2014, 22.9 per cent of the population were children – approximately 19 per cent higher than both the regional and national averages.

- In 2014, 13.1 per cent of people living in Birmingham were of pensionable age – lower than both the regional (18.0 per cent) and national (17.6 per cent) averages.

- The key reasons for population growth in Birmingham City are an increase in the number of births, a rise in international migration and a declining death rate from improved health care.

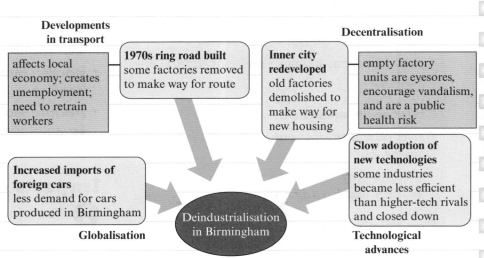

Developments in transport: affects local economy; creates unemployment; need to retrain workers

1970s ring road built some factories removed to make way for route

Inner city redeveloped old factories demolished to make way for new housing

Decentralisation: empty factory units are eyesores, encourage vandalism, and are a public health risk

Increased imports of foreign cars less demand for cars produced in Birmingham

Globalisation

Deindustrialisation in Birmingham

Slow adoption of new technologies some industries became less efficient than higher-tech rivals and closed down

Technological advances

Worked example

Study the graph opposite, which shows the projected change in broad age groups in Birmingham from 2012 to 2032.

Describe the projected trend illustrated on the graph.

(3 marks)

The graph shows that over the next 20 years the number of people in Birmingham aged 65 and above will rapidly increase, going from a 3 per cent change in 2015 to a projected 35 per cent change in 2031 compared with 2012. The age groups of 0–15 and 16–64 will level out over the same period of time, with a projected 10 per cent change.

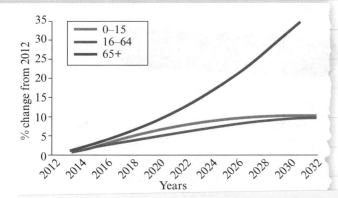

Projected percentage change of population age groups in Birmingham, 2012–2032

Remember when analysing a graph to look at the general pattern and anomalies. Try to refer to specific evidence in your answer.

Now try this

Explain **two** causes of deindustrialisation in UK cities. **(4 marks)**

City inequalities

Case study   You will need to know how economic change is increasing inequality in a named UK city, and what the differences in quality of life are.

Economic structure

Recent deindustrialisation and population increases have changed Birmingham's economic structure. The main reasons for economic change in Birmingham are the decline in manufacturing industry and lack of investment.

Deprivation is a way of measuring people's access to general resources and opportunities.

☑ 40 per cent of Birmingham's population live in areas that are among the most deprived in England.

☑ During 2004–2007 Birmingham was ranked as the most deprived local authority in the West Midlands.

☑ Sutton Four Oaks is in the top 5 per cent of **least** deprived SOAs in the UK.

☑ Deprivation is high in inner city areas of Birmingham, but also exists in the suburbs.

☐ in the most deprived 5% in England
▨ in the most deprived 10% but not the most deprived 5%
▨ in the most deprived 25% but not the most deprived 10%
☐ not in the most deprived 25% and non-residential areas

Areas of deprivation in Birmingham

SOAs are Super Output Areas, used to look at deprivation in small areas. Each SOA is awarded a score for different aspects of deprivation. In England there are 32 484 SOAs with populations of between 1000 and 3 200.

Differences in quality of life

some migrants don't have skills/qualifications for jobs available

increasing population density in inner city – strain on health services

provision of services – housing, schools – hasn't kept up with increasing demand

investment in inner city slow – limited public funding

Quality of life in Birmingham

available jobs often don't need specific skills/qualifications but are short-term contracts

Worked example

Remember to take your time when looking at a graph. Use a ruler to check the figures!

Study the graph of SOAs in major UK cities.
Which city has the lowest percentage of most deprived 25% SOAs in England?   **(1 mark)**

Bristol

Percentage of SOAs in major cities in the most deprived 25%, 10% and 5% in England.

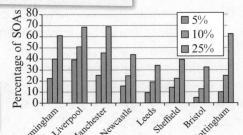

Now try this

Describe the distribution of SOAs in Birmingham to show areas of deprivation.   **(3 marks)**

Retailing changes

 Case study You will need to know about recent changes in retailing and the impact they have had on a named UK city.

Birmingham's changing CBD

19th century
People move away from city to suburbs to avoid increasing pollution levels

→

1870s
Manufacturing industries relocate to suburbs

→

1970s/80s
Shopping outlets move to edge- and out-of-town locations like Merry Hill

Decline in CBD

As Birmingham's CBD has declined, so has retailing there. To address this the city council has supported redevelopment projects including the Bullring and Grand Central shopping centres.

Grand Central shopping centre aims to bring consumers back to the CBD

New shopping centres

Edge- and out-of-town centres have advantages:

- **for retailers** – cheaper, larger units than in CBD
- **for consumers** – free, easy parking; all stores under one roof

Rise of internet shopping

The rise in internet shopping since the late 1990s has reduced numbers of consumers using the CBD. Benefits include:

- 24-hour shopping
- special discounts
- 'armchair' shopping

Worked example

Explain how changes in retailing can have an impact on a city. **(3 marks)**

One of the impacts of changes in retailing on cities in the UK is the decline in traditional town centre businesses, due to the movement of larger brands to out-of-town locations. This leaves many town centres with empty retailing units and declining services for people.

This answer provides a clear explanation of one of the impacts changes in retailing are having on cities.

Impact of decentralisation in Birmingham

- The movement of shops to out-of-town locations like Merry Hill caused a 12 per cent decline in trade in the CBD.
- The movement of shops to Merry Hill resulted in the redevelopment of what was originally a brownfield site.
- Redevelopment of the CBD through new projects like the Mailbox and Bullring has now seen a growth in trade.

Now try this

Suggest how internet shopping can impact on retailing in cities. **(2 marks)**

City living

 Case study You need to know how a named UK city can use a range of strategies to make urban living more sustainable and improve quality of life.

Worked example

Explain the strategies used by a UK city to improve sustainability. **(4 marks)**

One of the strategies used by Birmingham City Council to improve sustainability is encouraging people to use public transport, car share, walk and cycle around the city. The city council has supported the use of hybrid buses, which could save 378 tonnes of carbon every year.

Birmingham has also improved its recycling system to reduce waste sent to landfill sites. It now recycles around 30 per cent of its waste, although this is still less than the national average of 40 per cent.

 This answer clearly focuses on how two strategies have helped to improve sustainability, with clear use of supporting evidence.

Employment and education

✓ Youth **unemployment** in Birmingham has reduced in recent years, from 12 per cent in 2014 to 9 per cent in 2015. The council has introduced the Youth Promise pledge that aims to provide employment, education and training for those aged 14–25.

✓ The city council works closely with schools and universities through the Birmingham Education Partnership to recruit and retain teachers. The city has 17 teaching schools – one of the highest numbers in the country.

Housing and health

In February 2016, Birmingham announced a new £59 million project to improve the **energy efficiency** of homes:

✓ The city council plans to improve insulation in people's homes by installing new windows and more efficient heating systems

✓ Residents' monthly bills will be lower and the city's CO_2 emissions reduced.

✓ The city is working with Healthy Villages to improve the **health and wellbeing** of its residents by improving access to services.

Affordable housing

- Birmingham Municipal Housing Trust and Capita have been working together to build new affordable housing for residents.
- A total of 1576 houses have been built across different areas of the city under this scheme.
- In 2015, a new affordable housing development was started in Solihull with the building of 13 one-bedroom and 14 two-bedroom apartments.

New affordable housing like this has been built in Kings Norton, Newton and Northfield.

Now try this

Explain **one** strategy used by a city to improve standards of living.
(2 marks)

63

Context and structure

 Case study You will need to know the site, situation, connectivity and structure of a chosen city in a developing or emerging country. Here we will look at Mexico City – a major city in a developing country.

Mexico City

Site – began as a settlement on an island in Lake Texcoco in Aztec times (14th–16th century).

Situation – located on the Central Plateau, a flat landscape surrounded by mountains and volcanoes.

Connectivity – major highways make it the main link between North and South America. It is the national base for theatre, TV and radio.

Culture – Mexico City is the largest Spanish-speaking city in the world.

Worked example

The following statements describe the characteristics of Mexico City's structure. Identify **two** statements that best describe Mexico City's Central Business District (CBD).   **(2 marks)**

☐ **A** Characterised by slums
☐ **B** Characterised by middle-class housing
☒ **C** The main financial hub of the city
☒ **D** It attracts high-value retailers

In geography the **site** is the type of land used to build a settlement. The **situation** is the position of a settlement in terms of the physical and human features that surround it.

Mexico City structure

CBD – main financial hub characterised by office blocks, including Mexican Stock Exchange and government buildings. Now attracts high-value retailers.

Inner city – characterised by slums. First slums built during the 19th century.

'Vecindades' are abandoned multi-storey colonial mansions converted into cheap tenements and rented out to families.

MEXICO CITY

Suburbs – areas like Ciudad Satélite, characterised by middle-class housing, mainly built to owners' orders.

Tight security – walled-off parking spaces, barbed wire, electric fences and armed guards.

Ciudad Satélite

Vecindades in Mexico City

Urban–rural fringe – land use dominated by unregulated shanty towns.

Now try this

Explain the **site** and **situation** of an emerging or developing city.   **(3 marks)**

A rapidly growing city

Case study You will need to know the reasons for past and present trends in population growth for a city in a developing or emerging country as well as the causes of national and international migration and their impacts.

Population growth

During the 1950s Mexico City's population was approximately 2 million. By 2010 the urban area had a population of approximately 19 million.

The annual growth rate of Mexico City has also changed over time, from 5.5 per cent during the 1950s to only 0.8 per cent by the year 2000.

Greater Mexico City is the most populated metropolitan area in the Western Hemisphere.

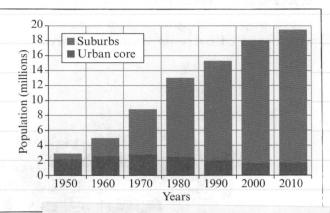

Population growth in Mexico City's urban core and suburbs, 1950–2010

Causes of population growth

Over the years, population growth in Mexico City has been caused by different factors.

1 **Natural increase** – during the 1950s a high birth rate and a fall in the death rate meant the population grew rapidly.

2 **National and international migration** – see below.

3 **Economic investment** – increased job opportunities through investment in the construction of factories and offices in the city.

National migration is movement of people within a country. International migration is movement of people to a different country.

National and international migration

The main flow of migrants to Mexico City is from rural areas (national), with people looking for alternative jobs to farming, better housing, clean water and improved health care.

Fewer migrants arrive from the USA, Germany and France (international) and tend to live in the wealthier parts of the city.

Impacts of migration on the city

• need for homes has led to more self-built housing at the city edge – larger shanty towns

• greater use of open space – higher population density and greater poverty

• many migrants moving to the city are young adults, leading to a rise in the number of younger people living in the city – but the lack of jobs is increasing the rates of crime

• rise in car ownership is increasing both air and noise pollution, causing health problems

• fear of crime is leading to segregation of people, with the wealthier living in gated communities

• difficulties in supplying clean water with rising demand, putting pressure on the city's reservoirs and underground aquifers.

Worked example

Explain **one** cause of population growth for a city in a developing or emerging country. **(2 marks)**

One of the main reasons for population growth in Mexico City is rural–urban migration, caused by the lack of job opportunities and poor housing in the countryside.

Now try this

Study the graph above. Describe the patterns of population growth in Mexico City's urban core and its suburbs. **(3 marks)**

Increasing inequalities

 Case study For a city in a developing or emerging country you will need to know how rapid urban growth is causing inequalities and what its wider-scale impacts are.

Extreme wealth vs poverty

Rapid population growth has resulted in inequalities between rich and poor, with areas of extreme wealth and areas of extreme poverty.

Mexico City CBD

Shanty town in Mexico City

- **Wages**: minimum wage should be US$4 per day, but about 1 in 3 workers are paid less. In the CBD wages are much higher, with the top 20 per cent earning as much as 13 times more than the bottom 20 per cent.
- **Education**: the poorest 10 per cent average only two years of school attendance, while the richest 10 per cent average 12 years.
- **Services**: shanty town residents have no running water, electricity or food shops, unlike residents in wealthier areas who live in large houses with gardens and swimming pools.

Worked example

Explain **two** impacts of rapid urbanisation for a city in a developing or emerging country. **(4 marks)**

One of the impacts of rapid urbanisation in Mexico City is pollution. The city has more than 3.5 million cars moving around on a daily basis, causing high levels of air pollution. Also, the city is unable to cope with the volume of waste produced every day, resulting in waste being dumped on streets and polluting water supplies. This creates a second impact: the spread of diseases like cholera and typhoid from sewage leaking into the water supply.

This answer provides two clear impacts, with accurate case study evidence to support the points made.

Impacts of rapid urbanisation

Housing shortages – many migrants moving to the city are living on garbage dumps, forced to search through the waste to make money.

Squatter settlements – migrants from the countryside are forced to illegally build homes made out of waste materials on the edge of the city. These homes have no running water or electricity.

Under-employment – these are the people who work seven days a week doing more than one type of job.

Pollution – Mexico City is surrounded by mountains, so pollutants are trapped. This increases air pollution, causing many people to suffer from respiratory diseases.

Inadequate services – the city generates 13 000 tonnes of rubbish every day but struggles to dispose of all of it, with waste dumped on the streets.

Now try this

Define the term 'squatter settlement'. **(1 mark)**

Solving city problems

🌐 **Case study** For a city in a developing or emerging country you will need to know the advantages and disadvantages of bottom-up and top-down development projects to help solve the city's problems and improve quality of life, as well as the role of government policies.

- **Top-down projects** are large-scale projects usually funded and managed by city governments.
- **Bottom-up projects** are small-scale projects often funded by NGOs (non-governmental organisations) or community organisations.

Community-based projects

A number of community-led projects have been established in Mexico City, including:

1 Cultiva Ciudad is working with local schools to educate children about managing a garden.

2 Rooftop gardens have taken off, with residents growing healthy foods.

3 Locals are working together on the outskirts of the city to raise money to help build schools and health centres.

Affordable housing

Architect Tatiana Bilbao has designed an affordable style of housing to help solve the housing problems in Mexico City. The US$8000 homes are made from wooden pallets that can be added or removed as required.

Sustainable transport schemes

- In 2005, Mexico City's government introduced Metrobus, estimated to reduce 35 000 tonnes of CO_2 emissions annually.
- The bus rapid transport system moves approximately 250 000 people per day.
- The new transport system has reduced average journey times by 30 minutes – from 1.5 hours to 1 hour.

Waste recycling

Mexico City produces an estimated 13 000 tonnes of solid waste every day, with all the waste being sent to one landfill site. This landfill site was eventually shut but the government failed to provide an alternative.

In 2011, to combat this issue, the government introduced a trading system – trash for food.

A 'barter market' was set up with residents exchanging waste for vouchers. These vouchers were then traded with local farmers for food.

Worked example

Explain the different approaches used to solve the problems faced by a city in an emerging or developing country. **(4 marks)**

Mexico City has introduced a sustainable transport scheme called Metrobus. The new scheme is able to move 250 000 people per day around the city and is believed to help reduce 35 000 tonnes of CO_2 emissions every year. The city has also introduced a 'barter market' to encourage its residents to recycle waste. Residents bring their waste to the market and exchange it for vouchers to buy food.

You should be able to write confidently about a number of top-down and bottom-up development projects for your chosen city.

Now try this

You have studied a major city in a developing or emerging country. Evaluate the success of different development projects used to improve the lives of people living in the city. **(8 marks)**

Defining development

There are contrasting ways of defining development, and different factors contribute to the development of a country.

What is development?

Development is a term that measures how advanced a country is compared to another. It is about the standard of living in a country – whether people can afford the things they need to survive. However, it's not just about money. Development also includes the quality of life within a country.

How a low-income country might develop

- Investment in farming – higher yields to eat and sell.
- Electricity grid reaches rural areas.
- New roads or railways – connect remote areas with cities.
- Literacy rises – better job prospects.
- Gender equality improves.

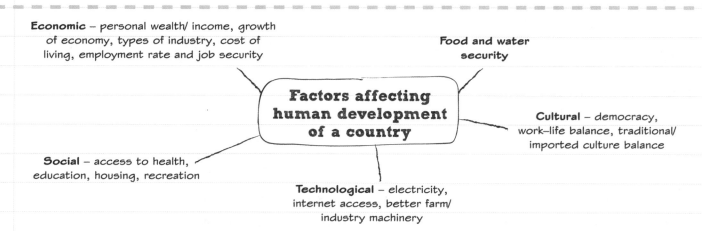

Economic – personal wealth/ income, growth of economy, types of industry, cost of living, employment rate and job security

Food and water security

Factors affecting human development of a country

Cultural – democracy, work–life balance, traditional/ imported culture balance

Social – access to health, education, housing, recreation

Technological – electricity, internet access, better farm/ industry machinery

Food security

An imbalance between **food production** and **food consumption** means many countries lack **food security**. This means people lack:

- **availability** – of enough food all the time
- **access** – to enough of the right food to stay healthy
- **knowledge** – to make the best use of what they have.

Worked example

Explain how water security contributes to the human development of a country. **(3 marks)**

Access to safe water kick-starts human development. Safe water improves people's lives as they are no longer too ill to work, children can go to school and women can work instead of spending all day fetching clean water.

One in nine people in the world do not have access to safe water. Approximately 2 million people die from water-related illnesses every year.

Now try this

Explain **one** factor, other than access to safe water, that contributes towards the human development of a country.

(2 marks)

Measuring development

Development is measured in different ways, including Gross Domestic Product (GDP) and the Human Development Index (HDI). There are also measures of inequality and indices of political corruption.

The level of development in a country or region can be measured using statistics for:

- **economic** indicators
- **social** and **political** measures.

Some things are easy to measure (e.g. birth rate). Others are harder to measure (e.g. how safe people feel).

Rank	GDP (US$ million)	GDP per capita (US$)	HDI
1	USA (17 348 071)	Monaco (187 650)	Norway (0.944)
2	China (10 430 589)	Lichtenstein (157 040)	Australia (0.935)
3	Japan (4 602 419)	Luxembourg (116 650)	Switzerland (0.930)
4	Germany (3 868 291)	Qatar (97 519)	Denmark (0.923)
5	UK (2 988 893)	Norway (97 226)	Netherlands (0.922)

Top five countries by various development measures.

Bhutan measures its Gross National Happiness.

Development indicators

- **GDP – Gross Domestic Product** is the total value of goods and services produced by a country in a year. It is often divided by the population of that country to give **GDP per capita** (per person).
- **HDI** – the **Human Development Index** puts together a country's Gross National Income (like GDP per capita), life expectancy and average years in education to produce an indicator of the country's development level.

These have limitations because:

- all measures of development show averages only
- data do not show everything and are not always accurate. For example, GDP doesn't include the cash economy.

Political corruption

Quality of government has a big impact on development. The Corruption Perceptions Index grades the quality of governments from 'highly corrupt' to 'very clean'.

Remember: if a question says **explain one** then don't explain more than one point.

Worked example

Explain **one** way of measuring economic inequalities within a country.   **(2 marks)**

One way of measuring economic inequalities is to use the Gini coefficient. This is expressed as a ratio from 0 to 1. Same income for everyone = 0; one person has all the income = 1.

Now try this

Define the term 'GDP per capita'.   **(1 mark)**

Remember: with a **define** question, you only need to say what the geographical term means.

Patterns of development

Globally, development is uneven. A range of factors has led to variations in the level of development **between** countries and **within** countries – including the UK.

Worked example

Describe the global pattern of GDP per capita as shown on the choropleth map opposite. **(3 marks)**

The general pattern shows higher GDP per capita tends to be found in countries in the northern hemisphere, with the USA having one of the highest GDP per capita at US$50000–60000. The lowest GDP per capita tends to be found in the southern hemisphere, especially in central Africa.

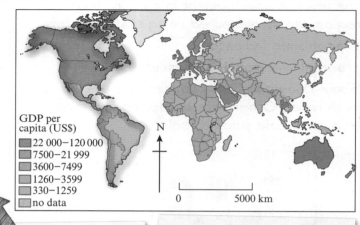

GDP per capita (US$)
- 22 000–120 000
- 7500–21 999
- 3600–7499
- 1260–3599
- 330–1259
- no data

World map showing GDP per capita (US$), 2014.

When a question asks you to describe a pattern, describe the general trends, rather than listing specific details.

Variations in the UK

Development levels vary within the UK. In London and South East England, people generally have a higher standard of living than people in the rest of the UK.

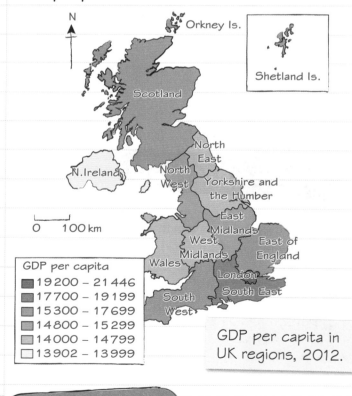

GDP per capita
- 19 200 – 21 446
- 17 700 – 19 199
- 15 300 – 17 699
- 14 800 – 15 299
- 14 000 – 14 799
- 13 902 – 13 999

GDP per capita in UK regions, 2012.

Factors affecting development level

Global inequalities

- **Physical** – size of country, natural hazards, landlocked or not, tropical or temperate climate
- **Historical** – colonial links, trading relationships
- **Economic** – type of economy, debt, investment in health and education

Inequality within the UK

- **Physical** – remoteness or accessibility of area, the potential for industry
- **Historical** – links with particular industry, impact of **deindustrialisation**
- **Economic** – employment rates and salaries, house prices, state of infrastructure

In the UK the decline of industries (**deindustrialisation**) during the second half of the 20th century led to rising unemployment levels.

Now try this

Describe the pattern of GDP per capita shown on the choropleth map of the UK above. **(3 marks)**

Uneven development

Uneven global development has had different impacts on people's quality of life in different parts of the world.

Uneven impact

Jobs in the informal sector, like street stalls, are less secure and have fewer benefits.

Lack of water limits people's ability to grow the food they need.

Employment in developing countries is limited, with people working in lower paid, more labour-intensive jobs.

Developing countries lack access to food and clean water, resulting in malnourishment and dehydration.

Food and water security

Appropriate technology can be more effective in meeting local needs in a sustainable way.

Healthcare is limited in the developing world, with fewer doctors and poor facilities.

Employment

Health

Uneven impact

Technology

Less investment in technology, with few people who have the skills to use it.

Access to housing

Education

Many people around the world don't have access to housing.

Literacy rates are low in the developing world, with few schools and poor attendance rates.

More than 30 per cent of the world's population live in slums. Each year, more than 6 million children die before they reach their fifth birthday.

People with the least education have the largest families, which can lead to debt and malnutrition.

Worked example

For this type of question you will need to develop your points – just as the example does by mentioning 'forced to walk miles' and 'contracting diseases like cholera'.

Suggest **one** of the consequences of uneven development. **(3 marks)**

One of the consequences is that many people have a low quality of life. For example, while most people in more developed countries have easy access to clean water, many people in developing countries lack this, and are forced to walk miles to drink dirty, contaminated water. This leads to people contracting diseases like cholera, which lowers life expectancy.

Now try this

Describe **one** impact that uneven global development has on education. **(2 marks)**

International strategies

A range of international strategies (international aid and inter-governmental agreements) attempts to reduce uneven development.

International aid

International aid is where one country voluntarily transfers resources to another country. It provides vital income for many poor countries, and helps reduce uneven global development. It can:

- pay for imports, e.g. machinery and oil, which are vital to development
- support the accumulation of enough capital to invest in industry and infrastructure
- address a shortage of the skills needed for development.

```
                        international aid
                       /                \
        official government aid ───→ ←─── voluntary aid
              /          \
    multilateral aid   bilateral aid
              \          /
        short-term        long-term
     emergency aid     development aid
```

Aid and debt relief are agreed between governments.

Inter-governmental agreements

These are agreements made between two or more governments to cooperate in some way.

Trade

Trade agreements such as removing trade barriers can reduce uneven development by helping developing countries to increase trade: for example, open trading between the EU and China.

Fair trade

Fair trade producers in developing countries work together to deal directly with retailers in developed countries, get fairer conditions and get a better price for their goods. Fair trade makes up less than 1 per cent of total world trade.

Foreign direct investment (FDI)

FDI is when a company invests in a company in a different country, and has some control over what that company does.

- 👍 Brings in investment
- 👍 Brings in big brands – widens consumer market
- 👍 Foreign companies may be able to pay more – pushes up wages
- 👎 Big brands can outsell local products
- 👎 FDI not always reliable – investors can pull out
- 👎 Lack of regulation can have negative implications, e.g. environmental consequences and industrial accidents

Worked example

Explain how debt relief can be used as a strategy to reduce uneven global development. **(3 marks)**

Many of the world's poorer countries struggle to make the annual repayments associated with debt. In 1996, the IMF and World Bank organised the HIPC (Heavily Indebted Poor Countries) initiative to reduce the amount owed by these poorest countries. This has helped to release some of the countries' income to be used to improve the lives of their residents.

A question with the command word **explain** and 3 marks is asking you to develop a point. You could use specific examples, as in the answer above.

Now try this

Explain **one** way that international aid can reduce uneven global development. **(3 marks)**

Top-down vs bottom-up

Development projects can be top-down (led by government or transnational corporations – TNCs) or bottom-up (led by the community). Each approach has advantages and limitations when it comes to promoting development.

Top-down development

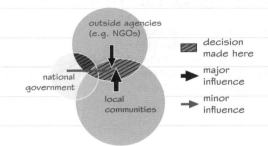

- Top-down development happens through actions of governments and TNCs
- Large-scale projects that aim at national-level or regional-level development
- Very expensive projects often funded by international development banks
- Sophisticated technology that needs experts to install and maintain

Bottom-up development

- Bottom-up development happens through actions of NGOs working with communities
- Local-scale projects that aim to benefit a village or small group of communities
- Very cheap compared to top-down, but usually funded by the community
- Appropriate technology that local people can learn to operate and repair

How successful is top-down development?

👍 Can access very large sums of money through investment from TNCs that also provide knowledge and expertise for further projects

👍 Can benefit thousands of people

👍 Access to world-leading experts and latest technology

👎 Funding can come with 'strings attached', e.g. remove trade barriers

👎 Many local people may not benefit, e.g. if they have to move because a major new dam project will flood their village

👎 Investment from TNCs can lead to poorly paid employment, which reduces people's chances of breaking the poverty cycle

Worked example

Explain the advantages and limitations of bottom-up development projects in the promotion of development.   **(4 marks)**

One of the advantages of bottom-up development projects is that they can be targeted at the specific needs of local people: for example, supplying clean water from a new well. On the other hand, the use of these projects can mean that the promotion of development is slow, because governments in poorer countries rely on the work of NGOs to develop solutions.

This answer provides one clear advantage and one clear limitation – with supporting points.

Now try this

Explain the limitations of using top-down development projects in the promotion of development.   **(4 marks)**

Location and context

🌐 **Case study** You will have studied development in a developing or emerging country. You need to know how your country has been influenced by its location and context, and understand the broad political, social, cultural and environmental context of the chosen country, in its region and globally.

India's location in the world

The southern part of India borders on the Indian Ocean. Inland, India shares its international borders with six countries: Bangladesh, Burma, Bhutan, Nepal and Pakistan.

India has two island groups: the Andaman and Nicobar Islands, and the Lakshadweep Islands.

Lakshadweep Island

Andaman and Nicobar Islands

India is in the Northern Hemisphere and is located in the continent of Asia. It is one of the largest countries in the world by area.

India in context – political

India is a member of global groups including the World Trade Organization and the United Nations.

- **Regional** – India is the largest country in the Indian subcontinent.
- **Regional** – most of India's population live in the six states of Maharashtra, Madhya Pradesh, West Bengal, Bihar, Andhra Pradesh and Uttar Pradesh.
- **Global** – India is the second most populated country in the world – 1.31 billion people in 2015.
- **Global** – India is the seventh largest country in terms of **area**.

India in context – social

- **Regional** – population is divided over 29 states: Rajastan = largest, Goa = smallest.
- **Regional** – social ranks known as 'castes', assigned at birth, divide India's society.
- **Global** – over 20 million Indian **diaspora** (scattered groups) are located in approximately 100 countries.
- **Global** – India's globally-spread population generates income for its economy with money sent back (remittances).

India in context – cultural

- **Regional** – over 80 per cent of India's population are Hindu.
- **Regional** – other religions in India include Islam, Sikhism and Buddhism.
- **Global** – India has the third-largest Muslim population in the world.
- **Global** – India's film industry, Bollywood, makes 1600 films a year, seen by 2.7 billion people.

Worked example

Describe **one** environmental context of a developing or an emerging country. **(2 marks)**

India experiences two monsoon seasons – the north-east monsoon occurs during the cooler months and the south-west monsoon during the warmer months.

What do you know about the regional and global contexts of your country?

Now try this

Describe the cultural context of an emerging or developing country. **(2 marks)**

Uneven development and change

Case study   Development does not take place at the same rate across all regions of a country. You need to know about the pattern of development in the core and periphery of your chosen developing or emerging country. You also need to understand types of changes that have taken place in the different sectors of the economy.

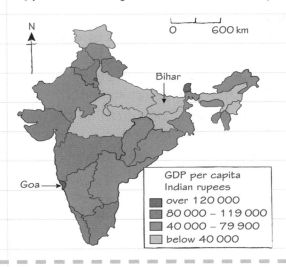

GDP per capita Indian rupees
- over 120 000
- 80 000 – 119 000
- 40 000 – 79 900
- below 40 000

Unevenness of development

Development can be uneven within a country, varying between **core** (most economically advanced) regions and the **periphery** (regions with lower development).

- Goa – a core state: 140 000 Indian rupees GDP per person; where investment has been focused on emerging industries
- Bihar – a state in the periphery: 23 435 Indian rupees GDP per person; often lower due to the harsher physical environments

India's GDP per person, 2011–2012

Changes in economic sectors

Since India's independence in 1947 there have been rapid changes in its economic sectors.

Sector	Changes	Impacts
Primary extraction/production of raw materials	• contribution of agriculture to India's GDP down from 58 per cent to 26 per cent • increased mechanisation	• rural–urban migration as more people move in search of work • breakdown of traditional family unit
Secondary manufacturing of raw materials	• slow industrialisation = secondary sector contribution to GDP up from 15 per cent to 22 per cent	• rising air pollution • increased population density in cities • widening development gap between urban and rural areas
Tertiary providing services	• increased from 27 per cent to 52 per cent during the same period	• increased employment opportunities • growth of India's economy with rising GDP and GNI
Quaternary providing information services – like computing	• fastest-growing telecom markets in the world – with second-largest wireless network	• increased investment from TNCs • over 1 million new ICT jobs created

Make sure you know about the impacts of economic changes in the country you have studied.

Worked example

Explain why development occurs at different rates across the regions of the developing or emerging country you have studied. **(4 marks)**

In India, the 'core' economic regions have developed more rapidly than the 'periphery' economic regions. In core regions like Gujarat, dynamic industries have created a high volume of exports, which has brought wealth and jobs to the region, helping it to develop rapidly. In peripheral regions like Bihar, incomes are low and most people still depend on agriculture as there is very little manufacturing industry, so the rate of development has been much slower.

Now try this

Explain the impacts of **two** economic changes in a named developing or emerging country. **(4 marks)**

Trade, aid and investment

🌐 **Case study** The development of a country can be affected by economic, social and demographic processes, and the way these processes interact with each other. For the developing or emerging country you have studied you need to know about changes in its economy, its involvement in international trade and aid, and about public and private investment.

India's top five merchandise import and export partners

exports
imports

India's trading characteristics

- During the 1990s changes in India's trading policies led to a rapid rise in **imports** (goods coming in) and **exports** (goods going out).
- In 2014, India was ranked 19th in the world for exporting merchandise.
- In 2014, India was ranked 8th in the world for exporting commercial services.
- India's key exports by value are oil products, gems and jewellery.
- India's key imports by value are crude oil, gold, silver and electrical goods.

As India has developed, international aid to the country has decreased. India now sends aid to other countries, such as Nepal. Most of the aid India receives goes to its poorest areas or to improve infrastructure.

Worked example

Study the graph opposite, which shows the international aid given and received by India, 2004–2015.

Describe the trend shown on the graph. **(3 marks)**

From 2004 to 2012 international aid received remained considerably higher than aid given, with a significant rise during 2010–2011. By 2014, aid given by India was US$750 million higher than aid received.

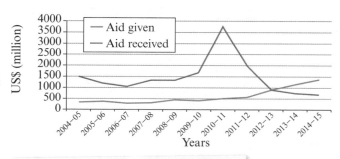

Foreign aid given and received by India, 2004–2015

Public vs private investment

Public (investment by the government)		Private (investment by TNCs or smaller businesses)
Public investment – in areas such as education, health, transport and housing – is important for development. Many people work in India's public sector, which is still bigger than in the UK or USA. Since the 1990s, India has reduced the divide between the public and private sectors.		Private investment by TNCs and smaller businesses has been key to India's economic development and has increased.

Now try this

Look at the trade flow maps above. Describe the trade flows of exports from India. **(4 marks)**

Changing population

Case study The development of a country can be affected by both demographic and social processes. For the developing or emerging country you have studied you need to know about changes in its population and life expectancy over the last 30 years, as well as changing social factors.

Changing population structure

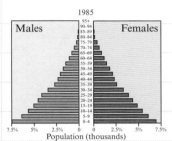
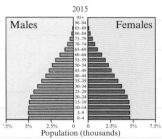

Make sure you understand what different population pyramid shapes represent.

In 1985 India's population was 782 million; by 2015 it had increased to 1.3 billion.

India's population has increased by 68 per cent since 1990. In the last 30 years the population structure has changed significantly, with:

- a smaller proportion of people under 15
- more economically active people (15–64)
- more people aged 65+.

Do you know the population changes for your case study country?

Life expectancy in India

Life expectancy has improved over the last 30 years, rising from 54 years in 1985 to 68 years in 2015.

Two key factors are:

- reduced infant mortality rate – fewer children dying before 5 years old
- reduced maternal mortality rate – fewer mothers dying in childbirth.

Life expectancy is the average age men and women live to.

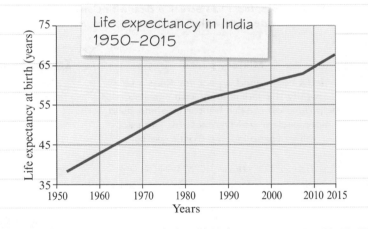

Life expectancy in India 1950–2015

Changing social factors

Increased inequality
- Wider gap between rich and poor
- Continuing low status of poorer women
- Older people not benefitting from progress

Growing middle class
- Urbanisation + education = growing middle class
- Growing consumer market – could be world's biggest by 2030

Improved education
- Greater investment in schools – high government priority
- Literacy rate has risen
- Strong private education sector

Worked example

Study the graph of life expectancy in India, 1950–2015. Describe the trend shown on the graph. **(3 marks)**

The graph shows India's life expectancy has increased rapidly, rising from 37 to 66, an increase of 29 years. The increase slows down slightly between 1980 and 2010.

When describing trends, remember to support your points with evidence from the graph.

Now try this

Explain how changing social factors are having an impact on a developing or emerging country. **(4 marks)**

Geopolitics and technology

Case study Changing geopolitics and technology can have an impact on a country's development. For the developing or emerging country you have studied you need to know about the effects of geopolitical relationships with other countries, as well as how technology and connectivity are supporting development.

Geopolitics

Geopolitics is the impact of a country's human and physical geography on its international politics and relations.

For example, Japan and China are economic rivals; Japan has worked to build strong political relations with India, China's economically powerful neighbour.

Top 10 most powerful countries

1 USA	6 UK
2 China	7 Brazil
3 Japan	8 Italy
4 Germany	9 Russia
5 France	10 India

What do you think makes a country 'powerful'?

Foreign policy

India's new foreign policies include building links with leading countries like France, Canada and Germany to encourage more investment in defence, energy and infrastructure. For example, India has struck a deal with Canada for it to provide India with 3.2 million kilos of uranium.

Defence

India is in discussions with the USA for a defence agreement to provide shared logistics for warships, fighter planes and personnel, which could help provide humanitarian assistance and disaster relief.

Military pacts

India has signed a pact for Russia to supply the Indian army with missiles, help develop stealth fighter jets and build more nuclear power reactors. The pact will increase income from exports.

Impact of India's relationships

Territorial disputes

India is in competition with China over water resources on the Yarlung Tsangpo–Brahmaputra River. Building dams could limit each other's supply of hydro-electric power and water. Disputes with Pakistan over the territory of Kashmir have led to a series of wars.

You need to know how changing geopolitics affect your chosen country.

Technology and connectivity

India's technology has expanded fast. It now has the world's second-largest wireless network, and its own high-level ICT industry. However, there's a **digital divide** between:

- core and periphery
- urban and rural.

In 2013, more than half of India's 61 million broadband connections were in just five of its 29 states.

Worked example

Study the socio-economic data below for India's core and periphery regions.

Calculate the mean literacy rate for the four states. **(1 mark)**

State	Literacy rate (%)	GDP per capita (Rupees)	Drinking water (% of population served)
Goa	79	168 572	85
Maharashtra	80	83 471	68
Bihar	64	20 708	4
Uttar Pradesh	77	26 355	27

75%

To calculate the mean, add all percentages together, then divide the total by the number of figures.

Now try this

Explain how technology has supported development in different parts of a named developing or emerging country.

(4 marks)

Impact of rapid development

Case study When development is rapid, the impacts on the people and environment of a developing or emerging country can be positive and negative. For the developing or emerging country you have studied you need to know about the social, economic and environmental impacts of rapid development and how these are being managed by the country's government and people.

Environmental

👍 Potential to invest in technologies – renewable energy

👎 Logging and land clearance – deforestation

👎 Increased CO_2 emissions – climate change

👎 More chemicals used in industry/agriculture – water pollution

👎 Desertification and deforestation – lower biodiversity

Social

👍 Better access to healthcare – lower infant mortality

👍 Better jobs and income – reduced poverty

👍 Improved community spirit from newly formed groups

👎 Pollution in cities – poor public health

👎 Lack of housing – slums and shanties

👎 Men/young people benefit most – women/older people left behind

Impact of rapid development

Economic

👍 Rise in consumerism – strong economy

👍 Increase in tourism – jobs and state income

👍 Larger workforce

👎 Cost of dealing with environmental and social problems

👎 Cost of installing new infrastructure

👎 Pressure and cost to provide more services

Worked example

You have studied a named developing or emerging country. Explain how its government is managing the impacts of rapid development in order to improve its global status. **(3 marks)**

India is the world's third largest emitter of greenhouse gases, mainly caused by rapid development. In order to improve its resulting negative global status and to help reduce climate change, the Indian Government has agreed to develop renewable energy resources. The Intended Nationally Determined Contribution (INDC) focuses on clean energy such as solar power and promises to plant more forests to absorb carbon emissions.

India is responsible for 5.8 per cent of global greenhouse emissions.

Now try this

Explain how **one** impact of rapid development is being managed to improve the quality of life in a developing or emerging country. **(4 marks)**

The world's natural resources

The world's natural resources can be defined and classified in different ways but the environments in which they are found are at increasing risk from human exploitation.

Types of natural resource

1 Biotic resources

- Obtained from the biosphere
- Capable of reproduction
- Examples: animals, birds and plants

2 Abiotic resources

- Obtained from the lithosphere, atmosphere and hydrosphere
- Examples: minerals, soil, sunlight and fresh water

3 Non-renewable resources

- Combustible sources that can't be 'remade'
- Formation takes millions of years
- Examples: coal, oil, uranium and natural gas

4 Renewable resources

- Potentially inexhaustible
- Can be naturally replenished
- Examples: wind, solar and hydro-electric power (HEP)

Exploiting environments: oil extraction in Ecuador

- ✓ **1960s** Texaco discovers oil in Oriente region and builds 350 oil wells.
- ✓ 1000 open unlined pits filled with toxic sludge were left behind; 18 billion gallons of toxic water dumped into rivers, reducing water quality.
- ✓ Local tribes rely on rivers for drinking, cooking, bathing and fishing.
- ✓ Drinking polluted river water leads to increased reports of miscarriages and birth defects.

Exploiting environments: overfishing in the North Sea

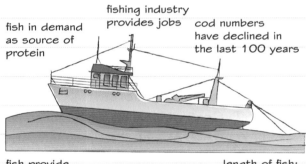

fish in demand as source of protein

fishing industry provides jobs

cod numbers have declined in the last 100 years

fish provide protein and employment

unsustainable fishing practices – more caught than replaced

length of fish: 2m in 1915; 35cm in 2012

Deforestation in Cameroon

- Cameroon rainforests have high biodiversity – 600+ species of trees and bushes
- 70 000 hectares cleared or being cleared to make way for palm oil plantations – extensive soil erosion
- Biodiversity under threat – some of the oldest woodlands on Earth at risk.

Worked example

Explain **one** impact of farming on the environment. **(2 marks)**

Large-scale clearing of natural habitats for intensive monoculture farming alters the environment by reducing biodiversity and may lead to species extinction.

> This is a good answer as it links farming to the exploitation of the environment.

Now try this

Use joining words such as **whereas** to **compare**.

Compare the differences between renewable and non-renewable energy. **(3 marks)**

Variety and distribution

Natural resources are not evenly distributed and you will need to know the variety and distribution of the world's and UK's natural resources.

Worked example

Study the world map. Describe the global distribution of copper. **(3 marks)**

The map shows that the world's copper resources are in Europe, Africa, Oceania, North America and South America. South America has one of the highest copper reserves in a line along the west coast. There are also large amounts of copper in South Africa.

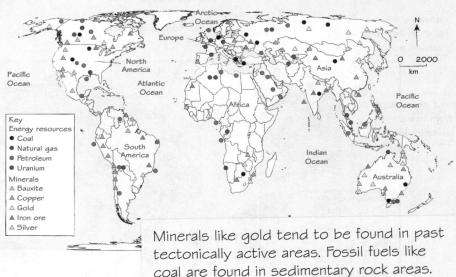

Global distribution of minerals and fossil fuels

Minerals like gold tend to be found in past tectonically active areas. Fossil fuels like coal are found in sedimentary rock areas.

Agriculture and forestry: influence of latitude

- Higher precipitation and solar radiation near Equator. Very productive. TRF, forestry and plantation agriculture. Soil infertile: latosols.

- Colder and drier at the poles. Low productivity. Tundra/coniferous trees. Forestry. Soils leached. Type of soil is podsols.

- 30° N and S of Equator, high solar radiation, very low precipitation. Little or no vegetation. Nomadic herding. Irrigated crops. Desert sandy soils.

The UK's natural resources

1 **Precipitation** is higher in the north and west (low population density) compared to the south (high population density).

2 Types of **agriculture** depend on soil, climate and relief. East Anglia has flat land, fertile soils and warm summers so is suitable for arable farming, e.g. wheat. Sheep farming is located in upland areas like Scotland.

3 **Oil and gas** are extracted from the North Sea. Billions of barrels are produced each year.

Now try this

Study the map below, which shows the distribution of different types of agriculture in the UK.

Describe the distribution of hill sheep farming. **(3 marks)**

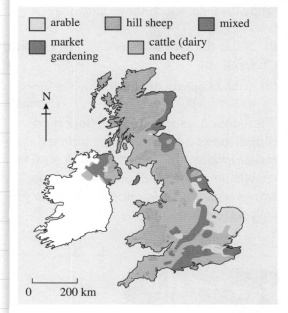

Global usage and consumption

Food, energy and water are vital for human survival, but their usage and consumption are not evenly distributed across the world.

Differences in usage and consumption

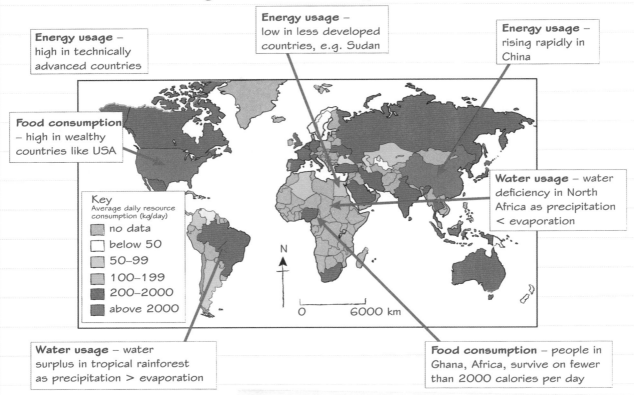

Energy usage – high in technically advanced countries

Energy usage – low in less developed countries, e.g. Sudan

Energy usage – rising rapidly in China

Food consumption – high in wealthy countries like USA

Water usage – water deficiency in North Africa as precipitation < evaporation

Key
Average daily resource consumption (kg/day)
- ☐ no data
- ☐ below 50
- ☐ 50–99
- ☐ 100–199
- ☐ 200–2000
- ☐ above 2000

N

0   6000 km

Water usage – water surplus in tropical rainforest as precipitation > evaporation

Food consumption – people in Ghana, Africa, survive on fewer than 2000 calories per day

Average daily consumption of resources is 90 kg per person in North America, but only 10 kg per person in Africa.

Worked example

Study the map, which shows global use of fuels.

(i) Name this type of map. **(1 mark)**

Choropleth

(ii) Explain **one** reason for the uneven global use of fuels. **(2 marks)**

The uneven use of fuels is linked to global development. Rapid industrial development in countries such as China results in higher fuel use than areas where industrial development is very limited, such as most of Africa.

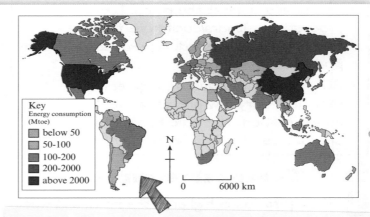

Key
Energy consumption (Mtoe)
- ☐ below 50
- ☐ 50-100
- ☐ 100-200
- ☐ 200-2000
- ☐ above 2000

N

0   6000 km

When you are asked to use a map, look at the key carefully to help you give an accurate answer.

Now try this

Which of the following is the energy consumption in Mtoe for the UK? **(1 mark)**

☐ **A** 50 ☐ **B** 100–200 ☐ **C** 200–2000 ☐ **D** over 2000

Production and development

There are advantages and disadvantages to renewable and non-renewable energy resources, in terms of their production and development.

In this component you must study **either** Energy resource management **or** Water resource management. **Only revise this section if it is the one you have studied.**

Non-renewable energy resource – example: coal

👍 Very productive resource – generates large amounts of energy

👍 Still enough coal reserves to last 200 years+

Remember: energy resources can be renewable or non-renewable

See page 80 to read about their characteristics.

👎 Burning coal releases greenhouse gases into atmosphere

👎 Mining coal is dangerous – has caused many deaths

👎 Expensive to develop mines and opencast pits

Renewable energy resource – example: wind energy

👍 Harnessing wind energy doesn't pollute atmosphere

👍 Lowest-priced renewable resource

👎 Energy only produced when there is wind to move blades

👎 Installations can be unsightly on the landscape

👎 Relatively high cost to develop – turbine construction, site access roads, foundation and cabling costs

Worked example

Study the graph opposite.
Describe how global coal consumption has changed since 1980.   **(3 marks)**

From 1980 to 1990 the consumption of coal was fairly even for each of the continents, with the range between 0 and 1.5 billion short tons. This changed from 1990 with Asia's consumption of coal rising rapidly until it reached 5 billion short tons in 2010.

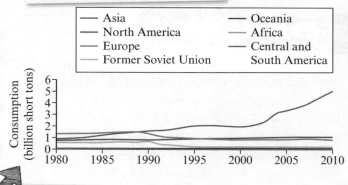

Global coal consumption, 1980–2010

— Asia   — Oceania
— North America — Africa
— Europe   — Central and
— Former Soviet Union   South America

Look for a general trend if you are asked to describe more than one line on a graph.

Now try this

Explain **one** advantage of developing a renewable energy resource.   **(2 marks)**

UK and global energy mix

Countries use energy resources in different proportions. This 'energy mix', and the demand for and supply of energy, varies due to a range of factors.

In this component you must study **either** Energy resource management **or** Water resource management. Only revise this section if it is the one you have studied.

Total UK primary energy consumption by fuel, 1970–2014

Legend:
- Coal
- Oil
- Gas
- Bioenergy and waste
- Primary electricity (including renewable electricity)

A changing energy mix

- During the 1970s the UK's reliance on coal and petroleum was high — 91 per cent of energy consumption.
- By 2014 this reliance had decreased — with a significant rise in renewable energy sources.
- Government has a target of 15 per cent of energy from renewable sources by 2020.

Global variations

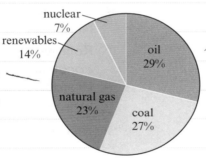

nuclear 7%
renewables 14%
oil 29%
natural gas 23%
coal 27%

Population China has a very large population and therefore relies on a variety/mix of energy types. Iceland has a small population and uses one energy type – geothermal power.

Wealth More developed countries (e.g. USA) can invest in a wider mix of energy types. Less developed countries cannot afford an energy mix (e.g. Pakistan depends on imported oil).

Availability Countries such as the UK are able to develop wind power/tidal power due to location. Other countries rely on imported oil and coal.

Worked example

Explain **two** reasons why the demand and supply of global energy resources has changed. **(4 marks)**

One of the reasons is improvements in technology. Compared to 100 years ago, households now own many electrical items like laptops, mobile phones and dishwashers, all needing electricity and increasing demand. A second reason for change is world population growth, along with economic development in countries like China and Brazil, increasing the need to meet the supply demands of their people.

Global demand and supply

There are three key reasons why demand and supply have changed in the past 100 years.

1. **Rapid population growth** – particularly in countries like China and Brazil.

2. **Rising affluence** – people more able to afford fuel resources.

3. **Advances in technology**
   - more electrical goods
   - renewable energy harnessed
   - development of new energy resources.

Now try this

Suggest means you must include some explanation in your answer.

Suggest **one** factor that causes global variations in the energy mix. **(2 marks)**

Impacts of non-renewable energy resources

The development of non-renewable energy resources like **coal**, **oil**, **natural gas** and **uranium** can have both positive and negative impacts on people and the environment.

In this component you must study **either** Energy resource management **or** Water resource management. Only revise this section if it is the one you have studied.

	Coal	**Oil**	**Natural gas**	**Uranium**
People	👎 Mining can cause subsidence of buildings. 👎 Miners at risk of illness and death.	👎 Leaks/spills expose people to harmful chemicals. 👍 Extraction process creates jobs locally.	👍 Safe = lighter than air and dissipates when there is a leakage.	👎 Damage from natural disasters = high risk of exposing people to radiation. 👎 Power stations expensive to build.
Environment	👎 Groundwater can become polluted. 👎 Burning coal produces large amounts of CO_2.	👎 Oil spillages = pollution of groundwater and drinking water. 👎 Land cleared for oil extraction = loss of farmland.	👍 Made from methane = fewer carbon emissions than other fossil fuels. 👎 Burning releases greenhouse gases = global warming and climate change.	👎 Waste highly radioactive = potential pollution from storing. 👍 Produces less CO_2 than burning fossil fuels.

Worked example

Study the diagram, which shows how shale gas extraction (fracking) works.

Suggest **one** way in which technology can resolve energy resource shortages. **(2 marks)**

In the UK geologists believe there is enough shale gas to provide energy for the next 70 years. The development of fracking, which uses new technology, will mean that the UK will not have to depend on imported gas.

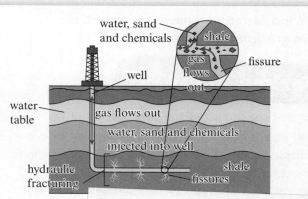

Fracking is not commercially carried out at present in the UK.

Now try this

Explain **one** negative impact of developing non-renewable energy resources on the environment. **(2 marks)**

Impacts of renewable energy resources

The development of renewable energy like **hydro-electric power (HEP)**, **wind power** and **solar power** has different positive and negative impacts on people and the environment.

> In this component you must study **either** Energy resource management **or** Water resource management. Only revise this section if it is the one you have studied.

Hydro-electric power (HEP)

To generate HEP dams need to be built, with positive and negative impacts.

People

👍 Could generate tourism, providing jobs for local people as guides.

👎 Building dams displaces people from their homes.

Environment

👍 HEP generates clean, non-polluting energy.

👎 Vegetation and forests may have to be removed in the construction process.

Xiluodu hydro-electric power plant, China

Wind power

People invest in wind power for eco-homes; countries like the UK invest in offshore wind farms, like the London Array.

People

👍 Offshore wind farms like the London Array can generate enough energy to power thousands of homes.

👎 Wind turbines installed on land can cause noise and visual pollution.

Environment

👍 Offshore wind farms like the London Array help to save thousands of tonnes of CO_2 each year.

👎 Wind farms can have an impact on migration patterns of birds.

Solar power

Development of this energy also has positive and negative impacts.

People

👍 More governments are investing in developing solar energy, creating jobs.

👎 Potential reduction in farmland for farmers to grow crops on.

Environment

👎 Many solar parks built in the desert – can damage fragile ecosystems.

👎 Constructing solar panels uses toxic metals like cadmium – can harm environment.

Worked example

Suggest **one** impact of the development of hydro-electric power on people. **(2 marks)**

The production and development of hydro-electric power can cause people to lose their homes and land to make way for the large-scale construction of the dam and reservoir.

Remember **suggest** means you must add an explanation.

Now try this

Explain **two** ways in which the development of renewable energy resources can have a negative effect on the environment. **(4 marks)**

Meeting energy demands

Renewable and non-renewable energy resources need to be managed and used sustainably. However, meeting and managing the world's growing energy demands involves different groups with different views on how to do this.

> In this component you must study **either** Energy resource management **or** Water resource management. Only revise this section if it is the one you have studied.

Why manage resources?

- Scientists say relying on fossil fuels could have irreversible impacts from climate change.
- Rising population and economic development means governments must increase supply from renewable resources.
- Individuals' impact can be measured using **ecological** and **carbon footprints**. People in the UK have an ecological footprint 4–5 times bigger than the global average!

Differing attitudes

- An example is the issue of fracking in the UK, with individuals protesting against the exploitation of shale gas due to its environmental impacts.
- In contrast, organisations see fracking in the UK as a financial benefit, generating money for industry and services and supported by the UK government.
- Pressure groups such as Greenpeace are opposed to fossil fuels, fracking and nuclear energy and want all energy produced by sunlight, wind, waves, tides and geothermal heat.

Individual

- More now using energy-efficient products and generating renewable energy, e.g. solar panels on roofs.
- Some feel renewable energy is too expensive (more than fossil fuels) – don't want higher energy bills.
- People living near proposed wind farms/solar parks may have concerns about noise and visual impact.

Organisation

- Many see importance of managing operations more sustainably – may advertise their actions for good PR.
- Increased operating costs may be a problem for small companies.
- McDonalds is an example of a company that has taken steps towards energy resource management through:
  - reuse of cooking oil from restaurants as biodiesel in delivery lorries
  - replacing neon and filament bulb lighting with LED lighting.

Differing views

Government

- World leaders' conferences have set shared targets and measures for sustainability.
- The UK and 195 other nations pledged to limit the increase in global temperature to 2°C at UN Climate Change Summit (2015), including investing in new low-carbon energy technologies.
- Many countries are adopting and encouraging citizens to use more sustainable transport systems with the introduction of congestion charging and bicycle schemes.

Worked example

Suggest **one** reason why people may not agree about the development of fracking to produce shale gas. **(2 marks)**

Some people and pressure groups do not think fracking is sustainable. They say reserves will only last for about 70 years and are non-renewable.

Now try this

Explain the different views held by individuals on the sustainable use of energy resources. **(4 marks)**

Explain means you need to make points and then give reasons.

China and Germany

🌐 **Located example** You will need to know how one developing or emerging country and one developed country have attempted to manage their energy resources in a sustainable way.

> Only revise this section if you studied Energy resource management.

Sustainable China (a developing country)

Background

- Contributes 29 per cent to global carbon emissions – more than any other country.
- Has seven of the world's ten most polluted cities.
- Burns more coal than USA, Europe and Japan combined.
- China Renewable Energy Law, 2006: aims to develop renewable energy resources.

Strategies

1 Hydro-electric power

Three Gorges Dam, China

In 2014, the Three Gorges Dam generated 98.8 billion kWh of electricity – roughly the same as burning 49 million tons of coal.

2 Solar power

- China is now a leading solar power producer.
- The solar plant being built in the Gobi Desert could produce energy for 1 million homes.
- Raised awareness of China's energy needs has increased take-up of solar panels.

3 Coal restrictions

- In 2015, the government introduced laws restricting use of heavily polluting coal in urban areas.

Sustainable Germany (a developed country)

Background

- 28 per cent of Germany's electricity produced from renewable resources.
- Target: to reduce greenhouse gas emissions by 40 per cent by 2022.
- Feed-in tariffs pay producers of renewable energy for electricity they produce.

Strategies

1 Solar power

Germany has invested in several solar parks.

Bavaria Solarpark

Bavaria Solarpark aims to produce 215 million kWh of clean power over the next 20 years, and reduce CO_2 emissions by 100000 tons over the next 30 years.

Worked example

Explain why one developed country is attempting to manage their energy resources in a sustainable way. **(4 marks)**

Germany is investing in finding technologies to increase efficiency of wind turbines. After the 2011 Japanese nuclear accidents, Germany's government developed a new plan for increasing renewable energy production, particularly offshore wind farms. A second reason for developing sustainable energy resources is that Germany plans to reduce greenhouse gas emissions by 40 per cent by 2022 to help reduce the impact of global warming.

> Include named examples and a concluding statement about their success in managing energy resources.

Now try this

Assess the success of countries at different levels of development in managing their energy resources in a sustainable way. **(8 marks)**

Global distribution of water

Water is an essential resource for human life but the availability of freshwater supplies varies globally.

In this component you must study **either** Energy resource management **or** Water resource management. Only revise this section if it is the one you have studied.

Global fresh water availability per person

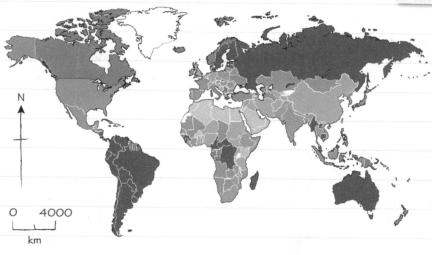

Fresh water availability (m³/person/year)

scarcity   stress   vulnerability

0   1000   1700   2500   6000   15 000   70 000   684 000

☐ data not available

- 97% of global water is saline (salty ocean water).
- 3% is fresh water suitable for human consumption, but 2% is locked up in glaciers and ice caps.
- Only 1% is available for our expanding global population!
- Places lacking water are usually near the Equator, especially North Africa.
- Canada and Iceland have the greatest fresh water availability per person.

Water surplus vs water deficit

Global water supplies are unevenly distributed because of variations in the amount of rainfall countries receive and the rate of evaporation and transpiration.

> Did you know that southern England has less water per person than Spain?

Tropical rainforests and mountainous areas receive more than they lose, resulting in a water surplus.

Countries in the Sahel region of North Africa receive little rainfall and have high rates of evaporation and transpiration, causing a water deficit.

Worked example

Define the term **water surplus**.   **(1 mark)**

Water surplus describes a place that receives more water from precipitation than is lost due to evaporation.

> Remember that with a **define** question you should give a brief statement.

Now try this

Study the map of global fresh water availability above. Describe the distribution of areas with water scarcity.   **(3 marks)**

Changing water use

Water supply and demand have changed in the past 50 years due to human intervention.

Only revise this section if you studied Water resource management.

Changing global patterns

- Asia (developing region) experienced the biggest increase from 1900, a dip after 1995, then an increase from 2010 onwards.
- North America and Europe (developed regions) experienced a slightly lower rate of increase from 1980, which has remained fairly stable.

- Africa and South America (developing regions) have lower water consumption but this has gradually increased since the 1970s.
- Oceania and Australia have the lowest water consumption by continent, and there is little change between 1900 and 2025.

Reasons for the pattern

As a country develops, the **standard of living** also increases. This leads to:

1. greater **mechanisation** in industry, using more water for manufacture (food and drink) and to cool down machinery

2. more **labour-saving devices** – washing machines use 80 litres of water per wash and dishwashers use 35 litres of water per wash

3. more water used for washing cars and watering gardens, and for luxuries like swimming pools and hot tubs

4. increased personal hygiene – we have moved towards **a showering society**, where people have regular showers, using 8 litres of water a day

5. increased leisure and tourism, with more water used in water parks, spas and for watering golf courses

Worked example

Study the graphs of world population and global water consumption. Compare the lines for total world population and world water consumption between 1950 and 2025. **(3 marks)**

Both the graphs show a significant increase between 1950 and 2025. The world's population seems to increase overall more rapidly than the water consumption graph. The water consumption graph shows a lower rate of increase between 1990 and 2010.

This answer gives three clear comparisons.

World population, 1750–2100

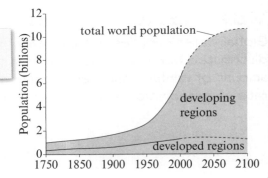

Global water consumption 1900–2025, by region in billion m³/year

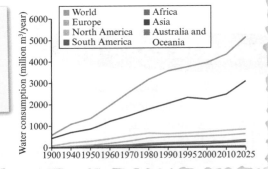

Now try this

Explain **two** reasons why the global demand for water has changed. **(4 marks)**

Water consumption differences

People use water for agriculture, industry and domestic purposes. There are differences between the water consumption patterns of developing countries and developed countries.

Only revise this section if you studied Water resource management.

Developed and developing countries

Average water consumption is an expression of the total water used in a country divided by its population. Water consumption in developed countries is high. On average, each person uses 1200 m³ per year. This is three times as much as in developing countries (400 m³).

- agriculture
- industry
- domestic

developed countries: 14%, 39%, 47%
developing countries: 5%, 4%, 91%

Water consumption in developed and developing countries

Reasons for differences in water usage

	Agriculture	Domestic	Industry
Developed countries	Drip feed sprinklers for watering crops control amount of water used. Automated irrigation systems use lots of water.	Piped water means people use lots of water for: • domestic appliances • baths and showers • toilets. Recreational use, e.g. swimming pools, hot tubs.	Water used for cooling machinery in factories.
Emerging and developing countries	Ineffective irrigation. Hand pumps limit water use. Surplus water left to drain away, evaporate or run off surface.	Communal taps and wells used for washing clothes. Bathe in rivers.	Small-scale industries, e.g. basket weaving and pottery, use very little water.

Key ▯ = low water use   ▯ = high water use

Study the divided bar chart below.

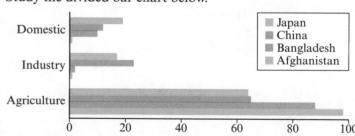

Domestic
Industry
Agriculture

- Japan
- China
- Bangladesh
- Afghanistan

0 20 40 60 80 100

Remember to use the scale – don't just guess.

Which country uses 19% of its overall water consumption in the domestic sector? **(1 mark)**
Japan

Now try this

Suggest reasons for the differences in water usage between developed and developing countries. **(4 marks)**

Water supply problems: UK

There are three key reasons why the UK experiences water supply problems – you will need to know all of them.

In this component you must study **either** Energy resource management **or** Water resource management. Only revise this section if it is the one you have studied.

Ageing infrastructure
Old water pipes can't cope with the higher water pressures needed now (3.28 billion litres/year); sewage pipes are similar.

Water supply problems in the UK

Seasonal imbalance
Some regions have greater difference between summer and winter rainfall than others, e.g. eastern Britain. Droughts cause problems for water supply companies, e.g. drier weather in 2009 = reduced reservoir levels in 2010.

Rainfall imbalance
Higher rainfall usually in upland areas (e.g. Scottish Highlands) with lower population density; lower rainfall in lowland areas (e.g. south-east, near London) where population density is higher.

Worked example

Study Figure 1, which shows water supply problems in England.

Water supply problems
■ Serious
■ Moderate
□ Low
□ Not assessed

North West
North East
West Midlands
East Midlands
South West
South
South East

Figure 1

1 Name a region with low water supply problems in England. **(1 mark)**

South West England

Other correct answers would be North West England and North East England

2 Describe the distribution of water supply problems in England. Use evidence from Figure 1 in your answer. **(4 marks)**

From the map, serious water supply problems seem to occur most towards the south and east of the map. The most serious issues are in the south and south-east, whereas the north-west and north-east are both low. The East and West Midlands are 'moderate', and it is only the south-west region with its low status which disrupts the north (low) and south (serious) pattern. This suggests that the further east, the more severe the supply problem.

Remember – in a **describe** question you do not need to **explain**.

Now try this

Look at the map in the Worked example.
Suggest reasons why some regions have serious water supply problems. **(3 marks)**

This question expects you to relate your answer to the map, so it is important that you look at the resource carefully.

Water supply problems: emerging or developing countries

Emerging or developing countries have their own water supply problems, including only having access to untreated water, pollution of watercourses and low annual rainfall.

> In this component you must study **either** Energy resource management **or** Water resource management. Only revise this section if it is the one you have studied.

1 Untreated water

- 663 million people – 1 in 10 – lack access to safe water.
- Developing countries in Africa are the most affected by a lack of safe drinking water.
- Without safe water, people cannot lead healthy, productive lives.
- Drinking polluted water causes water-borne diseases and parasites.
- An estimated 2000 people die every day from diarrhoea – governments can't afford water treatment schemes.

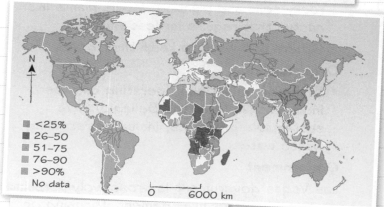

■ <25%
■ 26–50
■ 51–75
■ 76–90
■ >90%
No data

0   6000 km

Global access to safe water (percentage of population)

2 Pollution of watercourses

Water can become polluted because of:

- poor farming practices and unregulated use of fertilisers and pesticides
- mining, e.g. copper mining in Zambia in 2006 caused health problems
- lack of sanitation and education about human and animal faeces in water, leading to diseases.

3 Low annual rainfall

- Low annual rainfall can be the result of climate change, seasonal variations in climates and increasing population.
- Countries in the Sahel region have been subjected to repeated drought.
- Countries such as Chad and Mali suffer extreme water shortages.

Worked example

Study the photograph opposite. Explain **one** reason why people in developing countries may have to use untreated water. **(2 marks)**

One of the reasons why people in developing countries use dirty water is because they have no other choice due to lack of piped water. This means people often drink water that is polluted with animals and human faeces.

Water pollution in Africa

This is a developing area – include this information in your answer.

Now try this

Explain **two** ways watercourses in developing countries may become polluted.   **(4 marks)**

Attitudes and technology

Attitudes to the exploitation and consumption of water resources vary with different stakeholders: individuals, organisations and governments. Technologies such as desalination can resolve water-resource shortages.

> Only revise this section if it is Water resource management you have studied.

Attitudes to water exploitation: Las Vegas (Nevada)

Individuals

- Some are changing personal consumption, e.g by xeriscaping – replacing grass with rocky soils and planting desert plants like cactus that require far less water.
- Others still want to keep their grass.

Organisations

- Some organisations operating casinos in Las Vegas (e.g. the Bellagio) have sustainable practices, including recycling waste water.

Government

Las Vegas government is proactively pursuing sustainable water management, focusing on reducing domestic use by:

- paying residents to pull up lawns and replace them with desert gardens
- banning new houses from having grass in their front gardens.

> Make sure you use geographical terms, such as 'west'.

Worked example

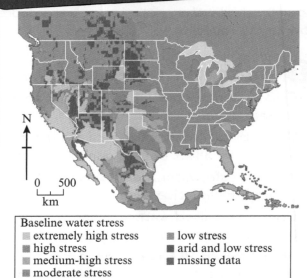

Baseline water stress
- extremely high stress
- high stress
- medium-high stress
- moderate stress
- low stress
- arid and low stress
- missing data

Study the map, which shows water stress levels in the USA.

Describe the location of areas with extremely high water stress. **(2 marks)**

The areas of high water stress are mostly in the west of the USA. There are also areas of extremely high water stress in the centre of the country.

Desalination

97% of global water is in the oceans. **Desalination** removes salt from seawater. This fresh water can then be used for drinking, agriculture and industry.

👍 Plentiful supply of saltwater

👍 No uncontrollable factors – only needs use of oceans

👍 Lessens demand on groundwater

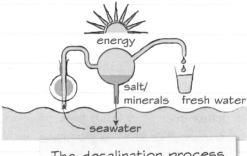

The desalination process

👎 High maintenance – equipment needs frequent cleaning

👎 Fish get sucked into desalination plants and killed

👎 Expensive set-up costs

Now try this

Suggest how attitudes to the exploitation and consumption of water vary between stakeholders. **(4 marks)**

Managing water

Management and sustainable use of water resources are required at a range of spatial scales, from local to international.

Why water resources need sustainable management

Water is fundamental to life, and is only renewable if it is managed in a sustainable way.

If we keep using our water resources in the same way, scientists estimate that:

- by 2025 two-thirds of the world's population could be living in water-stressed countries
- by 2030 the world will only have 60% of the water it needs.

> In this component you must study **either** Energy resource management or Water resource management. **Only revise this section if it is the one you have studied.**

Different attitudes in Las Vegas

Groups of people (stakeholders) have different views about the value of creating new water supplies. For example, Las Vegas has a water supply shortage and the government is proposing to pipe groundwater from eastern Nevada. This water will supply 300 000 homes.

Resident – I'm worried that water prices will rise and I won't be able to afford them.

Environmentalist – Removing groundwater will have significant impacts on eastern Nevada's ecosystems.

Businessman – I think this project will help to support Las Vegas' growing tourism industry. A lack of water will mean tourists won't come.

Government official – We have made significant progress towards water sustainability but if we don't continue forward with this project Las Vegas will not be able to meet the demands for water as the city continues to grow.

Farmer in Nevada – I rely on the groundwater supplies here to water my crops. This plan might leave me with not enough water.

Worked example

Define the term 'sustainable management'.   **(1 mark)**

Sustainable management means making sure present needs are met without compromising resources in the future.

> You may be asked to define key specification terms.

When a question asks you to **explain**, you need to give reasons about different views.

Now try this

Explain how views about the management and sustainable use of water resources can vary.   **(4 marks)**

UK and China

 Located example You will need to know how one developed and one emerging or developing country has attempted to manage its water resources in a sustainable way.

> Only revise this section if you studied Water resource management.

The UK (a developed country)

There's enough water to supply current and future demands, but uneven distribution of rainfall and population makes it hard to manage water supplies sustainably.

Water companies

Water companies can encourage sustainability by:

- treating wastewater for domestic and industrial reuse
- encouraging installation of water meters – reduces amount of water used
- educating people about need to save water and how to do this in their homes.

UK government

1 Supports private companies on how to be 'water neutral' – use no more water after development than before.

2 Changed building regulations to promote more water-efficient homes:
- water butts and drought-resistant plants
- more water-efficient dishwashers and washing machines
- low-flush or dual-flush toilets
- underground tanks to harvest rainwater and recycle greywater.

China (an emerging country)

China's rapid economic development has increased demand for water from industry and its population. Two-thirds of China's 669 cities suffer from water shortages.

Since 2011 China has developed ways to manage water use in urban areas more sustainably. By 2020 it plans to have:

- environmental protection for rivers and groundwater
- effective monitoring of water use
- highly efficient use of water in industry and irrigated agriculture.

China's achievements to date

Wastewater recycling – plants being built each week; Beijing recycles 85% of wastewater.

Storing rainwater – tanks in public buildings store rainwater; storm drains redirected to recharge groundwater stores.

Water-saving devices – devices on taps and toilets being fitted in homes.

Alternative farming methods – planting drought-resistant crops; straw in soil to retain moisture.

Wider monitoring – rice fields are watered when soil moisture drops to monitored level.

Technology – micro-sprinklers ensure water is directly used on plants.

Worked example

State **one** way an emerging or developing country has attempted to manage their resources in a more sustainable way. **(1 mark)**

China, an emerging country, has installed micro-sprinklers which mean less water is wasted when watering plants.

Now try this

Assess how countries at different levels of development manage their water resources in a sustainable way. **(8 marks)**

Remember to structure your answer with a number of clear examples and a concluding statement about their success.

Paper 2

Paper 2 focuses on the human environment, and has three sections: A, B and C. Each section has a range of different types of question, including an 8-mark extended writing question.

Paper 2 has three sections:

- **A: Changing cities**
- **B: Global development**
- **C: Resource management**

There will be one 8-mark extended writing question per section.

In **Section C** you only need to answer either **Question 4: Energy Management** or **Question 5: Water Management**, depending on which one you have studied.

SPGST

The extended writing question for **Section C** will be worth **8 marks + 4 marks for SPGST = 12 marks** in total.

With SPGST, the best answers will:

- use accurate spelling and punctuation
- follow the rules of grammar
- use a wide range of specialist terms appropriately.

Command words

In all sections of Paper 2 (A, B and C), the command word for the extended question will be either **assess** or **evaluate**.

Look back to page 55 for more on these command words and Assessment Objectives.

Assess and evaluate questions can draw on a resource, but don't always.

- Without a resource, they test Assessment Objectives 2 (4 marks) and 3 (4 marks).
- With a resource, they test Assessment Objectives 3 (4 marks) and 4 (4 marks).

Here is an example of an 8-mark question from **Section A: Changing cities**.

You have studied a major UK city and a major city in a developing or emerging country.

Evaluate which of these cities has been most successful in dealing with the impacts of rapid urbanisation on its people and the environment.

(8 marks)

Here is an example of an 8-mark question from **Section B: Global development**.

You have studied development in a developing or emerging country.

Assess the effects of changing geopolitical relationships with other countries on a named emerging or developing country. **(8 marks)**

Some points to get you started ...

- You could define urbanisation in your introduction.
- Consider the strengths and weaknesses of each city's approach to dealing with urbanisation.
- Make sure you clearly talk about people **and** the environment.
- Conclude by deciding which you think has been more successful and why.

Some points to get you started ...

- Think about both the positive and the negative effects of the country's different geopolitical relationships.
- Consider the different **types** of relationship – foreign policy, defence, military pacts and territorial disputes.
- Include specifics to support the points you make.

Now try this

Try the 8-mark question for either section A or section B above for yourself.

Remember that **assess** means consider the different factors involved **and** identify which are the most important; **evaluate** means measure the success of something **and** come to a judgement.

Formulating enquiry questions

You will have carried out two pieces of fieldwork. Fieldwork investigations allow you to apply your knowledge and understanding and learn new skills. Enquiry questions give your fieldwork a clear focus.

Enquiry questions in your exam

There are six stages in the enquiry process. You will be asked questions on **at least two** of them in the exam.

- **Develop a question**
- **Use a range of techniques and methods** These must include collecting data (**quantitative**) and making observations (**qualitative**).
- **Process your data** and **present your data**
- **Analyse and explain your data**.
- **Make conclusions**, using your data and written information.
- **Evaluate your data and data collection methods**.

There will be a choice of questions on coasts and rivers. If you did not do coastal fieldwork, go to page 101 for rivers instead.

- An enquiry question often relates to a geographical theory or case study.
- Key questions/hypotheses follow from the enquiry question and can be tested.

For example, an enquiry question could be:

- How and why does the shape of the beach at [location] change along a stretch of coastline?

A key question following on from this could be:

- Do the sediment size and shape change along the stretch of [location] coastline?

A hypothesis for this enquiry question could be:

- The sediment size decreases along the stretch of [location] coastline.

Worked example

Ordnance Survey Maps, © Crown copyright 2016, OS 100030901 and supplied by courtesy of Maps International

Explain **one** reason why site 5 is not appropriate for a study comparing beach sediment characteristics along one stretch of coastline. **(2 marks)**

Site 5 is located where the coastline changes direction, which means prevailing wind and wave direction and therefore longshore drift will be bringing different beach sediment to this coastline. As this is a different coastline in terms of processes and characteristics it cannot be used in this investigation.

Geographical examples and theories

You need to be able to identify the key geographical concepts that the investigation is based on.

For example, for the enquiry question:

- How and why do beach profiles vary in [coastal location]?

you need to understand that beach profiles are affected by:

- wave type
- wave frequency
- wave direction/ longshore drift
- local geology
- pebble size
- beach management strategies (e.g. groynes).

Now try this

The table shows beach profile data for a stretch of coastline. Calculate the mean beach profile angle. **(1 mark)**

Profile number	1	2	3	4	5	6
Profile angle in degrees	3.0	2.8	3.9	2.0	1.0	2.6

Methods and secondary data

You will have used several different fieldwork techniques and methods in your investigation. You need to know what these techniques and methods are appropriate for, and what things to watch out for when using them to avoid making errors in the field.

Worked example

Explain **one** reason why the method you used to measure the degree of roundness of beach sediment was appropriate. **(2 marks)**

Name of method used: Powers' roundness index

There were many pebbles of different amounts of roundness. I was able to visually compare these with the photos of pebbles ranging from very angular to well-rounded on the Powers' chart so my conclusions were not subjective. This method was appropriate because it was accurate and quick to carry out.

> You need to be able to say why the method you used was appropriate; there isn't just one correct method.

For your exam you will need to know and understand:

- one **quantitative** fieldwork method to measure beach morphology and sediment characteristics (quantitative methods record data that can be measured as numbers)
- one **qualitative** fieldwork method to record landforms that make up the coastal landscape (qualitative methods record descriptive data)
- the implications of coastal processes for people living near the coastal area.

> Sediment shape can be measured using the Powers' scale of roundness – very angular, angular, sub-angular, sub-rounded, rounded and well-rounded.

Worked example

Explain **one** way using a geology map supported your coastal investigation. **(2 marks)**

The geology map helped me to describe the landforms at Swanage Bay. The map told me that the headlands are made up of harder limestone and chalk and the bay is formed by softer clays and sands.

For your exam you will need to know about two secondary data sources:

- a geology map, e.g. BGS Geology of Britain viewer
- one other source, which your teacher is likely to suggest for you.

> Secondary data are data that someone else has already collected. You should be able to write about the advantages and disadvantages of your secondary sources and how these support your investigation.

Now try this

Study these two images. Which one shows a quantitative fieldwork method and which one shows a qualitative fieldwork method? **(1 mark)**

Using a clinometer to measure beach gradient

Using a questionnaire to collect data on coastal management

Working with data

You need to know about ways to process and present fieldwork data, analyse fieldwork data and make conclusions and summaries backed up by evidence from fieldwork data.

In your exam you may be asked questions about how the presentation of fieldwork data could be improved. It is unlikely that there will be mistakes in the presentation of the data. Instead, you should think about the advantages and disadvantages of different types of data presentation.

Worked example

A student used a line graph to compare distance along a beach profile and sediment size.

Explain **one** weakness of using a line graph to present this data. **(2 marks)**

A line graph is appropriate for presenting continuous data. Line graphs are used when time is one of the variables. Survey data involving categories, like this fieldwork data, is discrete data. Time is not a variable so this is not an appropriate method to present the data. A scattergraph could be used.

Top six data presentation disadvantages

1 **Scattergraphs** – can only show relationships between two variables, so inappropriate for more than two

2 **Pie charts** – lots of small segments make the chart difficult to interpret

3 **Choropleth maps** – hide variations within areas; give impression of boundaries between areas instead of gradual transitions

4 **Triangular graphs** – data must be in percentages

5 **Bar graphs** – do not show relationships between categories

6 **Cross-sectional diagrams** – only show a snapshot of the coastal profile at a specific time

Analysing data

Here are the key steps for successful data analysis.

1 **Describe** what you see.
- What are the overall patterns or main features?
- Are any figures in groups?
- Are there anomalies or exceptions?

2 Use **evidence** – precise figures from the data – in your analysis.

3 Give **reasons** for the patterns you see in the data.

4 Link these reasons to **geographical concepts**/theories you have already described.

Conclusions and summaries

In your conclusion you should go back to your key question or hypothesis, and use evidence from your investigation to answer it.

In the exam you may be asked to reflect on aspects of your investigation. You will need to either assess or evaluate.

- To **assess** you need to think about all the factors and identify the most important ones.

- To **evaluate** you need to weigh up the value or success of something, and come to a conclusion.

Graph showing relationship between beach height and sediment size

Now try this

Study the scattergraph, which shows beach height and sediment size for 10 sites. Describe changes in the relationship between the two variables. **(3 marks)**

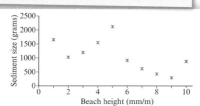

Formulating enquiry questions

You will have carried out two pieces of fieldwork. Fieldwork investigations allow you to apply your knowledge and understanding and learn new skills. Enquiry questions give your fieldwork a clear focus.

Enquiry questions in your exam

There are six stages in the enquiry process. You will be asked questions on at **least two** of them in the exam.

- **Develop a question.**
- **Use a range of techniques and methods.** These must include collecting data (**quantitative**) and making observations (**qualitative**).
- **Process your data** and **present your data.**
- **Analyse and explain your data.**
- **Make conclusions,** using your data and written information.
- **Evaluate your data and data collection methods.**

There will be a choice of questions on coasts and rivers. Only do the one that you did for your own fieldwork! **(If you did not do rivers fieldwork, go to page 98 for coasts instead.)**

- An enquiry question often relates to a geographical theory that can be tested through fieldwork: for example, the Bradshaw model (see diagram below), which shows how river characteristics change downstream.
- The enquiry question can be investigated by developing key questions or hypotheses.

For example, your enquiry question might be:

- How do river channel characteristics vary along the river [name]?

A key question following on from this could be:

- Does the width and depth of the river increase as the river flows downstream?

A hypothesis for this enquiry question could be:

- The width and depth of the river increase as the river flows downstream.

Worked example

Study Figure 1, which shows five sites selected by students along the Hawkcombe stream. The purple shading shows flood risk areas.

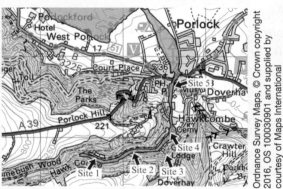

Ordnance Survey Maps, © Crown copyright 2016, OS 100030901 and supplied by courtesy of Maps International

Explain one reason why site 3 is not appropriate for comparing the impact of changing river discharge and flood risk with sites 1, 2, 4 and 5. **(2 marks)**

Site 3 is on a different tributary of the Hawkcombe, outside the flood area. Therefore including site 3 as part of data collection will give inaccurate data and lead to incorrect conclusions.

Geographical examples and theories

You need to be able to identify key geographical theories. For example, your enquiry question might be:

- How does river discharge vary with distance downstream?

You could use Bradshaw's model, which shows theoretical changes from source to river mouth.

upstream   downstream

channel depth
channel width   } needed to calculate discharge
mean velocity
discharge

Now try this

The table shows river velocity data collected by a student. Calculate the mean river velocity. **(1 mark)**

Site	1	2	3	4	5	6
Velocity (m/s)	0.16	0.41	0.38	0.05	0.08	0.51

101

Methods and secondary data

You will have used several different fieldwork techniques in your investigation. You should know why these were appropriate and how you made sure that your fieldwork was reliable and unbiased.

Worked example

Explain **one** reason why the method you used to measure stream velocity was appropriate. **(2 marks)**

Name of method used: A flow meter

It was appropriate because flow meters are the most accurate way of measuring velocity; unlike timing floating objects they are not affected by wind. I collected the data on a windy day, which would give incorrect results if I had used a surface float method, like a dog biscuit.

You need to be able to say why the method you used was appropriate for your fieldwork; there isn't just one correct method.

To calculate the discharge of a river you do the following:

area × velocity = discharge

For your exam you will need to know and understand:

- one **quantitative** fieldwork method to measure river discharge (quantitative methods record numerical data)
- one **qualitative** fieldwork method to record landforms forming the river landscape (qualitative methods record descriptive data, e.g. the appearance of river landforms)
- how river processes affect people living in a river catchment area.

Worked example

You have used a flood risk map in your investigation. Explain **one** way using the flood risk map supported your investigation.   **(2 marks)**

The flood risk map helped me choose suitable sites to study along the stream because it gave me information about the location of areas and property that had been flooded in the past.

For your exam you need to know about two secondary data sources:

- a flood risk map, such as an Environment Agency flood risk map
- one other source, which your teacher is likely to suggest for you.

Secondary data are data that someone else has already collected. You should be able to write about the advantages and disadvantages of your secondary sources and how these support your investigation.

Now try this

Study these two images. Which one shows a quantitative fieldwork method and which one shows a qualitative fieldwork method?   **(1 mark)**

Measuring water quality by sampling

Using a questionnaire to collect data on views about river flooding

Working with data

You need to know about ways to process and present fieldwork data including maps, GIS, graphs and diagrams (hand drawn and computer generated).

In your exam you may be asked questions about how the presentation of fieldwork data could be improved. It is unlikely that there will be mistakes in the presentation of the data. Instead, you should think about the advantages and disadvantages of different types of data presentation.

Worked example

A student investigated the relationship between river depth and river width.

Explain **one** advantage of using a scattergraph to present this data. **(2 marks)**

An advantage of a scattergraph is that it can be used to identify a relationship between two variables. It is easy to compare visually and a line of best fit can be drawn to indicate whether the relationship is positive, negative or whether there is no relationship.

Top six data presentation disadvantages

1 **Scattergraphs** – can only show relationships between two variables, so inappropriate for more than two

2 **Pie charts** – lots of small segments make the chart difficult to interpret

3 **Choropleth maps** – hide variations within areas; give impression of boundaries between areas instead of gradual transitions

4 **Triangular graphs** – data must be in percentages

5 **Bar graphs** – do not show relationships between categories

6 **Cross-sectional diagrams** – only show a snapshot of the river profile at a specific time

Analysing data

Here are the key steps for successful data analysis.

1 **Describe** what you see.
  - What are the overall patterns or main features?
  - Are any figures in groups?
  - Are there anomalies or exceptions?

2 Use **evidence** – precise figures from the data – in your analysis.

3 Give **reasons** for the patterns you see in the data.

4 Link these reasons to **geographical concepts**/theories you have already described.

Conclusions and summaries

In your conclusion you should go back to your key question or hypothesis, and use evidence from your investigation to answer it.

In the exam you may be asked to reflect on aspects of your investigation. You will need to either assess or evaluate.

- To **assess** you need to think about all the factors and identify the most important ones.
- To **evaluate** you need to weigh up the value or success of something, and come to a conclusion.

Now try this

Study the scattergraph showing river channel width for 10 sites. Describe changes in the channel width. **(3 marks)**

Graph showing river channel width for 10 sites

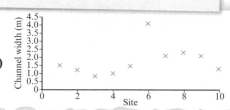

Formulating enquiry questions

You will have carried out two pieces of fieldwork. Fieldwork investigations allow you to apply your knowledge and understanding and learn new skills. Enquiry questions give your fieldwork a clear focus.

Enquiry questions in your exam

There are six stages in the enquiry process. You will be asked questions on **at least two** of them in the exam.

- **Develop a question.**
- **Use a range of techniques and methods.** These must include collecting data (**quantitative**) and making observations (**qualitative**).
- **Process your data** and **present your data.**
- **Analyse and explain your data.**
- **Make conclusions,** using your data and written information.
- **Evaluate your data and data collection methods.**

There will be a choice of questions on urban and rural areas. Only do the one that you did for your own fieldwork! **(If you did not do urban fieldwork, go to page 107 for rural fieldwork instead.)**

- An enquiry question often relates to a geographical theory that can be tested through fieldwork.
- Key questions/hypotheses follow from the enquiry question, which can be tested.

For example, an enquiry question could be:

- How does the quality of the urban environment vary along a transect through [urban area]?

A key question based on this might be:

- Does environmental quality vary along a transect from the CBD to the edge of [urban area]?

Study the photograph, which shows a central area in Reading. Give **one** reason why this is a suitable location for investigating the interaction of physical features and residents. **(2 marks)**

The photograph shows a physical feature, a river, that is going past some modern buildings. The river makes the area attractive for residents to walk along and to visit the new shops and offices. The land along the river is flat so it is easy for residents to walk there.

Geographical examples and theories

You need to be able to identify the key geographical concepts that the investigation is based on.

For example, for the enquiry question:

- How does the quality of the urban environment vary between the CBD and inner city areas in [urban area name]?

you could use theories such as urban land use models, which show variations in land use within an urban area.

Make sure you name at least one physical feature and say how it affects the urban residents.

Explain how you selected the locations to measure urban land use functions. **(4 marks)**

Methods and secondary data

You will have used several different fieldwork techniques in your investigation. You should know why these were appropriate and how you made sure that your fieldwork was reliable and unbiased.

Worked example

Explain **one** reason why the method you used to measure environmental quality in the urban area you studied was appropriate. **(2 marks)**

Name of method used: An environmental quality survey.

It was appropriate because using the same survey observations between sites allowed me to make meaningful comparisons.

> You need to be able to say why the method that you used was appropriate; there isn't just one correct method.

For your exam you will need to know about:

- one **qualitative** fieldwork method to record the quality of the urban environment (qualitative methods record descriptive data)
- one **quantitative** fieldwork method to measure land use function (quantitative methods record numerical data)
- the interaction between physical landscape features, the central/inner urban area and residents and visitors.

Worked example

You have used census data in your investigation. Explain **one** way using census data supported your investigation. **(2 marks)**

The census data gave me information such as the percentage unemployed in each ward, the percentage of people with no qualifications or with a degree. This information helped me to make a correlation between the levels of education and the environmental quality of each ward.

For your exam you will need to know about two secondary data sources:

- census data, e.g. Office for National Statistics (ONS) Neighbourhood Statistics
- one other source, which your teacher is likely to suggest for you.

> Secondary data are data that someone else has already collected. You should be able to write about the advantages and disadvantages of your secondary sources and how these support your investigation.

Worked example

You collected data on the perception of quality of an urban area but only collected data from females.

Explain **one** possible limitation of this data. **(2 marks)**

One possible source of error was my sampling strategy. I felt that men would be cross with me for asking them to do the survey questionnaire, so I didn't ask them. This created a bias of answers based on female perceptions. I did not have a true representation of local people's views about the quality of the urban environment.

You may be asked questions that require you to think about how effective your urban data methods were and any problems that occurred.

> For the exam, remember to revise disadvantages of your urban fieldwork methods.

Now try this

Create a table of the fieldwork techniques you used to measure the flows of people during your urban investigation. Explain **one** advantage and **one** disadvantage of each of the techniques.

(4 marks)

Working with data

You need to know about ways to process and present fieldwork data, analyse fieldwork data and make conclusions and summaries backed up by evidence from fieldwork data.

The exam may ask questions about how the presentation of fieldwork data could be improved.

It is unlikely that there will be mistakes in the way fieldwork data has been presented. Instead, you will need to use your knowledge of what the advantages and disadvantages are of different types of data presentation.

Top five data presentation disadvantages

1. **Scattergraphs** – can only show relationships between two variables, so inappropriate for more than two

2. **Pie charts** – lots of small segments make the chart difficult to interpret

3. **Choropleth maps** – hide variations within areas; give impression of boundaries between areas instead of gradual transitions

4. **Triangular graphs** – data must be in percentages

5. **Bar graphs** – do not show relationships between categories

Worked example

A student investigated variations in environmental quality in different urban locations. Explain **one** advantage of using a radar graph to present this data. **(2 marks)**

An advantage of a radar graph is that it can display data on several different variables such as housing quality so it is a good way to compare different environmental characteristics of an urban area.

Make sure you know the main types of data presentation method, and what they are best used for.

Analysing data

Here are the key steps for successful data analysis.

1. **Describe** what you see.
   - What are the overall patterns or main features?
   - Are any figures in groups?
   - Are there anomalies or exceptions?

2. Use **evidence** – precise figures from the data – in your analysis.

3. Give **reasons** for the patterns you see in the data.

4. Link these reasons to **geographical concepts**/theories you have already described.

Conclusions and summaries

In your conclusion you should go back to your key question or hypothesis, and use evidence from your investigation to answer it.

In the exam you may be asked to reflect on aspects of your investigation. You will need to either assess or evaluate.

- To **assess** you need to think about all the factors and identify the most important ones.

- To **evaluate** you need to weigh up the value or success of something, and come to a conclusion.

Now try this

Explain **one** advantage of the sampling strategy you used when measuring land use functions in an urban settlement. **(2 marks)**

Formulating enquiry questions

Enquiry questions are the kind of questions that can be investigated by fieldwork in rural environments. They give fieldwork a purpose. You will have put together enquiry questions for your fieldwork.

Enquiry questions in your exam

There are six stages in the enquiry process. You will be asked questions on at **least two** of them in the exam.

- **Develop a question.**
- **Use a range of techniques and methods.** These must include collecting data (**quantitative**) and making observations (**qualitative**).
- **Process your data** and **present your data.**
- **Analyse and explain your data.**
- **Make conclusions**, using your data and written information.
- **Evaluate your data and data collection methods.**

There will be a choice of questions on urban and rural areas. Only do the one that you did for your own fieldwork! **(If you did not do rural fieldwork, go to page 104 for urban fieldwork instead.)**

- An enquiry question often relates to a geographical theory: the sort of theory that can be tested through fieldwork.
- Key questions/hypotheses follow from the enquiry question, which can be tested.

For example, an enquiry question could be:

- Do traffic flows vary during the day in [rural settlement]?

A key question following on from this could be:

- How do flows of traffic entering and leaving [rural settlement] vary between 10am and 3pm?

Worked example

Study the photograph, which shows Lulworth Cove in Dorset. Give **one** reason why this is a suitable location for investigating the interaction of physical features and visitors. **(2 marks)**

Lulworth Cove is a beautiful physical location; it is a coastal area that people would want to visit. The car park is full so there would be plenty of visitors to answer questionnaires or take part in other surveys. The physical features such as hills also control the way people move around the area.

Make sure you name at least one physical feature and say how it affects visitors to the rural location.

Geographical examples and theories

You need to be able to identify the key geographical concepts that the investigation is based on.

For example, for the enquiry question:

- How does quality of life vary within rural settlements?

you might have used a questionnaire covering these key geographical concepts:

- decline in rural services
- rural housing prices due to second home purchasing
- low wages compared to urban areas.

Now try this

Describe **one** method you used to record the flows of people during your rural fieldwork. **(2 marks)**

Methods and secondary data

You will have used several different fieldwork techniques in your investigation. You should know why these were appropriate and how you made sure that your fieldwork was reliable and unbiased.

Worked example

Explain **one** reason why the method you used to measure environmental quality in the rural area you studied was appropriate. **(2 marks)**

Name of method used: An environmental quality survey.

It was appropriate because using the same survey questions between sites allowed me to make meaningful comparisons about the quality of the rural settlement based on residents' views.

For your exam you will need to know about:

- one **qualitative** fieldwork method to collect data about views of the quality of rural life (qualitative methods record descriptive data)
- one **quantitative** fieldwork method to measure the flows of people (quantitative methods record numerical data)
- the interaction between physical landscape features, rural settlements and residents and visitors.

You need to be able to say why the method that you used was appropriate; there isn't just one correct method.

Worked example

Explain **one** way census data supported your investigation. **(2 marks)**

The census data gave me information such as the percentage unemployed in each parish, the percentage with no qualifications or with degree-level qualifications. This information helped me to make a correlation between the levels of education and the people's views on the environmental quality of each parish.

The specification says that for the exam you need to know about two secondary data sources:

- census data, e.g. Office for National Statistics (ONS) Neighbourhood Statistics
- one other source, which your teacher is likely to suggest for you.

Secondary data are data that someone else has already collected. You should be able to write about the advantages and disadvantages of your secondary sources and how these support your investigation.

Worked example

You carried out a questionnaire survey to investigate views about the quality of a rural environment but only collected data from females. Explain **one** possible limitation of the data collected. **(2 marks)**

One possible source of error was my sampling strategy. I felt that men would be cross with me for asking them to do the survey questionnaire, so I didn't ask them. This created a bias of answers based on female perceptions. I did not have a true representation of local people's views.

You may be asked questions that require you to think about how effective your rural data methods were and any problems that occurred.

For the exam, remember to revise disadvantages of your rural fieldwork methods.

Now try this

Create a table for the fieldwork techniques that you used in **one** of your rural investigations. Explain **one** advantage and **one** disadvantage for each technique. **(4 marks)**

Working with data

You need to know about ways to process and present fieldwork data, analyse fieldwork data and make conclusions and summaries backed up by evidence from fieldwork data.

The exam may ask questions about how the presentation of fieldwork data could be improved.

It is unlikely that there will be mistakes in the way fieldwork data has been presented. Instead, you will need to use your knowledge of what the advantages and disadvantages are of different types of data presentation.

Worked example

A student investigated people's views about the quality of the rural environment. Explain **one** advantage of using a radar graph to present this data. **(2 marks)**

An advantage of a radar graph is that it can display data on several different variables so it is a good way to compare people's views about variation in environmental quality within a rural area.

Top five data presentation disadvantages

1 **Scattergraphs** – can only show relationships between two variables, so inappropriate for more than two

2 **Pie charts** – lots of small segments make the chart difficult to interpret

3 **Choropleth maps** – hide variations within areas; gives impression of boundaries between areas instead of gradual transitions

4 **Triangular graphs** – data must be in percentages

5 **Bar graphs** – do not show relationships between categories

 Make sure you know the main types of data presentation method, and what they are best used for.

Analysing data

Here are the key steps for successful data analysis.

1 **Describe** what you see.
  - What are the overall patterns or main features?
  - Are any figures in groups?
  - Are there anomalies or exceptions?

2 Use **evidence** – precise figures from the data – in your analysis.

3 Give **reasons** for the patterns you see in the data.

4 Link these reasons to **geographical concepts**/theories you have already described.

Conclusions and summaries

In your conclusion you should go back to your key question or hypothesis, and use evidence from your investigation to answer it.

In the exam you may be asked to reflect on aspects of your investigation. You will need to either assess or evaluate.

- To **assess** you need to think about all the factors and identify the most important ones.

- To **evaluate** you need to weigh up the value or success of something, and come to a conclusion.

Now try this

Explain **one** advantage of the sampling strategy you used when measuring the flows of people in a rural settlement.

(2 marks)

Consumption and environmental challenges

The UK's population will change in the next 50 years and there will be increased pressure on resources and ecosystems. What are the possible solutions to tackling sustainable transport?

Remember to revise topics from the rest of your geography studies that are related to this challenge.

Growing population

The UK is becoming overpopulated. There are too many people compared to the natural resources. For example, the UK only produces 60 per cent of its food.

By 2030, the UK's population is expected to rise to 70.5 million if current trends continue, due to natural increase and migration.

- 259 700 people from migration
- 226 200 from natural increase

In 2013, 25 per cent of births were to mothers born outside the UK.

> Be accurate! When taking readings from a graph, use a ruler.

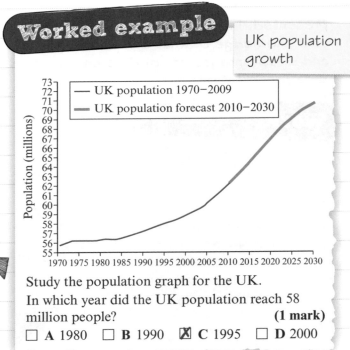

Worked example

UK population growth

Study the population graph for the UK.

In which year did the UK population reach 58 million people? **(1 mark)**

☐ A 1980   ☐ B 1990   ☒ C 1995   ☐ D 2000

Pressure on ecosystems

- potential rise in CO_2 emissions
- destruction of natural habitats
- building on greenfield sites
- **Pressure on resources**
- pressure on water systems
- food demands intensifying agricultural practices
- new houses potentially increasing flooding

Sustainable transport in the UK

- educating people to car share when commuting to work
- increasing public transport options
- implementing congestion charging and park-and-ride schemes
- new London taxis must be capable of zero emissions by 2018
- promoting the use of hybrid and electric cars

> Since the introduction of the congestion charging scheme in London, carbon emissions have reduced by 20 per cent within the zone.

Now try this

Suggest **one** way population growth puts pressure on ecosystems.   **(2 marks)**

Population and economic challenges

You will need to know the concept of the 'two-speed economy' in the UK, the costs and benefits of greenfield and brownfield sites, the UK net migration statistics and attitudes towards migration.

Remember to revise topics from the rest of your geography studies that are related to this challenge.

A 'two-speed economy'

This refers to the uneven growth of the UK economy, with the south-east developing faster. One possible solution to help bridge the gap between the south-east and the rest of the UK is improving transportation links with the north to encourage business development.

Greenfield sites

👍 The land tends to be cheaper for building

👍 More land development opportunities

👎 Potential loss of agricultural land

👎 Potential disruption to wildlife habitats and damage to ecosystems

Brownfield sites

👍 Services (like gas and water) are already installed

👍 Improvement to unused areas that are spoiling the landscape

👎 Potential restrictions to development

👎 Land tends to be more expensive

👎 Toxic substances may have to be removed

UK migration

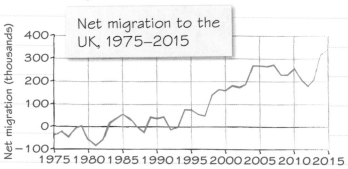

Net migration to the UK, 1975–2015

Migration statistics are estimates of the flow of migrants in and out of the UK.

Stakeholders have different views towards migration into the UK.

- Local councils have concerns about health and education provision.

- Businesses welcome migrants to increase the workforce as some migrants have skills that are in short supply.

- Some people believe migrants reduce the availability of employment.

During 2015, net migration was 336 000 people.

Worked example

Suggest **two** advantages of building on brownfield sites. **(4 marks)**

One of the advantages of developing brownfield sites is the removal of disused factories and the improvement of the aesthetics of the area. A second advantage is that infrastructure, such as roads, is already available, reducing development costs and timescales.

This answer gives two developed advantages and uses accurate specialist terminology.

Now try this

Using the graph above, calculate the range of net migration figures of migrants into the UK between 1975 and 2015.

(1 mark)

Landscape challenges

You will need to know the different approaches to conservation and development of UK National Parks as well as the approaches to managing river and coastal UK flood risk. Remember to revise topics from the rest of your geography studies that are related to this challenge.

The UK's 15 National Parks

N

0 100 km

Cairngorms
Loch Lomond and the Trossachs
Northumberland
North York Moors
Yorkshire Dales
Peak District
Norfolk Broads
South Downs
New Forest
Dartmoor
Exmoor
Pembrokeshire Coast
Brecon Beacons
Snowdonia
Lake District

Conservation and development

The management of the UK's National Parks is divided into different categories – habitats, biodiversity, climate change and historical environments.

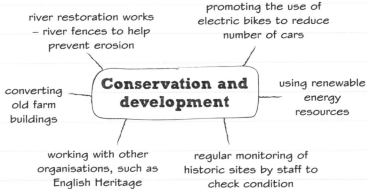

Conservation and development

river restoration works – river fences to help prevent erosion

promoting the use of electric bikes to reduce number of cars

converting old farm buildings

using renewable energy resources

working with other organisations, such as English Heritage

regular monitoring of historic sites by staff to check condition

Managing UK river flooding

The Environment Agency is responsible for the management of the UK's rivers and coasts.

The following approaches are used in river and coastal areas to manage flood risk (look back at pages 12 and 23 for more information on coastal and river management):

- monitoring and early warning systems
- soft and hard engineering techniques
- educating local residents
- new regulations for building on floodplains/coastlines
- river catchment management (afforestation).

The Thames Barrier is the largest moving flood barrier in the world! Its main purpose is to protect central London from flooding caused by tidal surges.

Now try this

Explain **two** different approaches to river flooding management in the UK. **(4 marks)**

Climate change challenges

You will need to know the different opinions on the potential impact of climate change on the UK in the future and the possible responses at local and national scales.

Remember to revise topics from the rest of your geography studies that are related to this challenge.

winter months   summer months

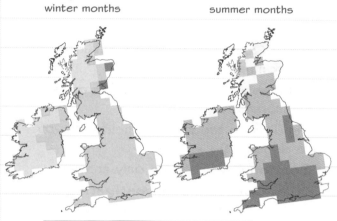

percentage change in precipitation

−60 −45 −30 −15   0   15   30   45   60

The UK's future climate

Future climate change could see the UK's temperature rising between 2°C and 4°C, causing warmer summers and winters.

Scientists also believe precipitation levels will increase and the UK will experience more extreme weather events.

> Percentage change in precipitation in the 2080s under the predicted high-emissions scenario.

Climate change could result in sea levels rising, causing extreme coastal flooding events. This will increase rates of erosion on coastal landforms.

By 2080, temperature increases could cause more frequent heatwaves and warmer winters, leading to periods of drought in the UK.

UK responses to climate change

Local scale: individuals can reduce their carbon footprint by using public transport, car sharing, recycling waste, and installing renewable energy resources.

National scale: the UK government can promote the use of more sustainable practices, raising awareness of adopting them to help tackle climate change. The UK government could also continue to invest in the increased use of renewable energy.

> Although this question doesn't ask for any specific examples, in a 3-mark question it's always a good idea to give at least two.

Worked example

Suggest how people can respond to climate change at a local scale. **(3 marks)**

One way people could respond to climate change is to swap the use of cars for public transport to help reduce greenhouse gases, such as CO_2. People could also install cavity wall and loft insulation to help reduce the amount of heat lost from homes. This reduces the use of fossil fuels (which cause climate change) to heat homes.

Now try this

Explain **one** potential impact of climate change.   **(2 marks)**

Paper 3 (i)

Paper 3 focuses on fieldwork and UK challenges. There are **two** 8-mark extended writing questions: one in Section A and one in Section B. **Section C has a 12-mark extended writing question – for more specific guidance on this question, see page 115.**

Paper 3 has three sections:

- **A: Geographical Investigations – Physical environments**
- **B: Geographical Investigations – Human environments**
- **C: UK Challenges (see page 115).**

For the 8-mark questions in **Sections A and B** you will be asked to apply your knowledge and understanding **either** in an answer about your own fieldwork **or** in an answer about fieldwork you did not do yourself.

If you are asked to apply your knowledge and understanding to fieldwork you did not do yourself, you will have resources to draw on, such as a map, graph, photo or some data.

Answering the right questions

In **Section A** you should only answer:

- either **Question 1: Investigating river environments**
- or **Question 2: Investigating coastal environments**

depending on the physical fieldwork you have done.

In **Section B** you should only answer:

- either **Question 3: Investigating human landscapes (central/inner urban area)**
- or **Question 4: Investigating human landscapes (rural settlements)**

depending on the human fieldwork you have done.

Command words and Assessment Objectives

In Paper 3 Sections A and B, the command word for the extended question will be either **assess** or **evaluate**. These questions may or may not have a resource for you to draw on.

Each of the 8-mark questions for Paper 3 tests Assessment Objectives 3 (4 marks) and 4 (4 marks).

Look back at page 55 for more on these command words and Assessment Objectives.

Here is an example of an 8-mark question from Section A, on your own fieldwork.

You have studied a coastal or river landscape as part of your own fieldwork.
Evaluate the reliability of the methods you used to collect your data. **(8 marks)**

For questions about **reliability** you need to talk about the different types of data collection methods you used and their advantages and disadvantages.

8-mark questions in Paper 3

You may be asked about your own fieldwork. For the best answers to these questions, you need to:

- carefully revise both of your fieldwork investigations
- make sure you are ready for questions on the difficult sections, e.g. how you used secondary data and the reliability of your conclusions.

You may be asked about fieldwork you did not carry out yourself. In this case, you will be asked to refer to a resource. For the best answers to these questions, you need to:

- read the question carefully; there may be important information, e.g. about sampling techniques
- make sure you look at all the resources carefully
- use information from the resources in your answers.

Now try this

Try the 8-mark question for Section A above for yourself.

Paper 3 (ii)

Section C of Paper 3 has an extended writing question worth **12 marks**, plus an **additional 4 marks for SPGST**.

For more on SPGST, see page 55 or page 97.

The 12-mark question

For this question, you need to draw on your knowledge and understanding across the different topics you have studied and apply these to a UK issue. You will also be given a **resource booklet**. You need to use information from the booklet **and** what you have learned to answer the question.

Command word

The command word for this question will always be **discuss**. With a **discuss** question, you need to:

- explore the different sides of an issue or question
- look at strengths and weaknesses of the different sides
- use well-thought-through reasons or arguments.

Assessment Objectives

The 12-mark question tests Assessment Objectives 2 (4 marks), 3 (4 marks) and 4 (4 marks). An **additional** 4 marks will be awarded for SPGST.

Look back at page 55 for more on these Assessment Objectives.

Worked example

Use the photographs and your own knowledge and understanding from the rest of your geography course of study to support your answer. Discuss the view that regeneration of brownfield sites is more beneficial than building on greenfield sites.

(12 marks + 4 marks for SPGST)

Remember there are **4 marks** for spelling, punctuation and grammar and your use of specialist terminology.

For brownfield sites one of the advantages is improving the look of the environment by removing or <u>doing up derelict buildings</u>. But building on a greenfield site can often mean the look of the natural landscape is <u>spoilt</u>.

A second advantage of brownfield sites is all things like <u>roads and gas are already there</u>. However, for greenfield sites these have to be put in.

Previous industry may have left <u>hazardous waste</u> on a brownfield site. Greenfield sites increase pollution because people <u>use their cars</u> to get to towns.

Try to use evidence from the photo, e.g. empty buildings/ boarded up windows.

Make sure this is specific – **how** has it been spoilt?

You could use photo evidence to help explain why this is an advantage.

Could you explain these points? Are they advantages or disadvantages in each case?

Now try this

Read the exam-style question and student answer above, and look at the annotations. Write an improved answer to the question, adding an introduction and a conclusion. Use the tips in the annotations to help you.

Your introduction for this question might define the key terms and your conclusion should provide a summary with a supporting judgement on whether it is more beneficial to build on brownfield sites.

Atlas and map skills

There are general geographical skills that you might need to draw on for any of the three exam papers. These include atlas and map skills. You will need to be able to describe the distribution and patterns shown on different kinds of maps.

Atlas maps

One of the most common types of map shows **distribution** – for example, the distribution of vegetation types, such as tropical rainforests.

■ rainforests of the world

Atlases also contain maps which show:

- **climate zones** and global variations in **precipitation** and **rainfall**
- country boundaries (political maps)
- **height** and **shape** of the land (**relief**)
- population distribution (how people are spread within a region or country).

> You may be required to use a combination of different types of information to answer a question.

Describing patterns

Ways of describing a **distribution, pattern** or **trend**

linear · dispersed · spaced · dense · clustered · scattered · uneven · sparse · irregular · even

You can also use the letters GSE to help structure your descriptions of patterns:

G – General overall trend or pattern

S – Specific examples that illustrate the trend or pattern

E – Exception: note any anomalies that do not fit in with the general pattern or trend.

> Don't fall into the trap of **explaining** why the pattern happens. Underline the command word in the question to help you focus your answer.

Worked example

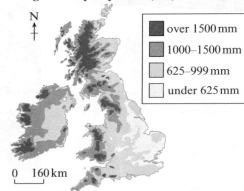

Average annual precipitation (mm)

N

- over 1500 mm
- 1000–1500 mm
- 625–999 mm
- under 625 mm

0   160 km

Study this figure, which shows the distribution of rainfall in the UK.

Describe the distribution of rainfall shown by the map. **(2 marks)**

Some parts of the UK, in the west and north, receive over 1500 mm of rainfall annually. The east of the UK is drier, with some parts of eastern England receiving less than 625 mm per year (average).

Now try this

Study the map above, which shows the global distribution of tropical rainforest.
Describe the global distribution of tropical rainforest. **(3 marks)**

Types of map and scale

You need to be able to recognise and describe the distribution and patterns shown by the variety of maps found in atlases, and deal with maps at a range of scales.

Satellite images and maps

Political maps which show the outline of countries

Rainforests of the world

Maps which show the **distribution** of vegetation type, e.g. location of tropical forests

Polar
Temperate
Arid
Tropical
Mediterranean
Mountains

Climate zones which reflect global variations in precipitation and temperature

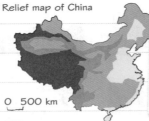

Relief map of China

0 500 km

level 1: 0–350 m
level 2: 351–1370 m
level 3: 1371–2500 m
level 4: 2501–5490 m

Relief maps showing the **height** and **shape** of the land

Persons per sq km
<20
20–99
100–179
180+

Population distribution maps which show how **spread** out people are within an area

Map scales

A map's scale tells you how much smaller the area shown on the map is compared to the area in real life.

- For OS maps at 1:25 000 scale, 1 cm on the map represents 25 000 cm (250 m) in real life.
- For OS maps at 1:50 000 scale, 1 cm on the map represents 50 000 cm (500 m) in real life.

Isoline maps

Isolines are lines that join points of equal value, such as height, depth or air pressure. Three common isoline maps are: OS maps, bathymetric ocean maps and air pressure maps.

Bathymetric ocean map

Worked example

Study the 1:25 000 Ordnance Survey map extract of Bolton Abbey.

How far is it from the car park at Bolton Bridge along the B6160 to the car park at Bolton Abbey? **(1 mark)**

☐ **A** 0.5 km
☒ **B** 1 km
☐ **C** 10 km
☐ **D** 10.5 km

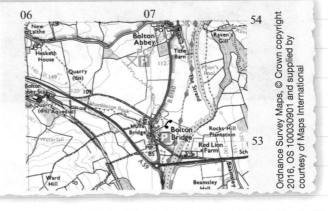

Ordnance Survey Maps, © Crown copyright 2016, OS 100030901 and supplied by courtesy of Maps International

Now try this

Study the 1:25 000 OS map extract of Bolton Abbey.
(i) Give the 6-figure grid reference for Bolton Abbey Station. **(1 mark)**
(ii) Give the 6-figure grid reference for the 109m spot height on the map. **(1 mark)**

Using and interpreting images

You should be able to respond to and interpret ground and aerial photographs and satellite images.

Different kinds of images

Ground-level photograph: shows lots of foreground detail. Use foreground and background to describe where things are in these types of photo.

Oblique aerial photograph: shows more of the area than a ground-level photo, and features are easier to identify than a vertical photo. But it is hard to judge scale for background features.

Satellite image: measures differences in energy radiated by different surfaces. False colour images convert this data into colours we can recognise. True colour images show us what the satellite sees, e.g. vegetation shows up red.

Vertical aerial photograph: these have a plan view, like maps. But details can be hard to identify.

Worked example

Study this aerial photograph of an open pit mine in South Dakota, USA. Identify **two** ways in which mining here has impacted on the landscape.

(2 marks)

Landscape scarring, removal of forests

Remember to study the photograph carefully before writing your answer. It has been given to you for a reason!

The Five Ws

When working with photos, be sure to remember the Five Ws.

What does the photo show?

Why was it taken?

Who are the people in it? (If there are people in the photo.)

Where was it taken?

When was it taken? (To indicate how long ago it was taken, what time of day, etc.)

Now try this

Suggest **one** advantage of using oblique aerial photographs instead of vertical aerial photographs.

(2 marks)

Sketch maps and annotations

Sketch maps are simple drawings of a place or area. You may need to draw, label or annotate a sketch map for any of the units you study.

Drawing sketch maps

Sketch maps can be drawn using information from a map or photograph, or drawn in the field. They:

- show where basic features are located
- have simple labels
- are often drawn from an **aerial** viewpoint
- can be annotated to add more explanation or detailed information.

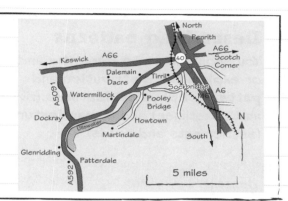

Sketching, labelling and annotating

- Photos and sketches are labelled and annotated in the same way.
- Only include the features that are relevant to the question.
- Draw clearly but don't worry about creating a work of art! Include a frame so that you can sketch within it.

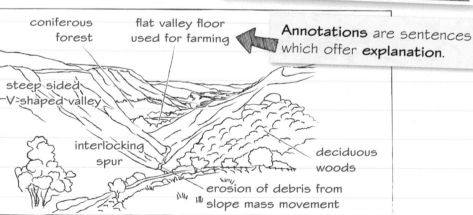

This is a sketch of the photo above with labels and annotations.

Labels are either one word or a short sentence which indicates what something is.

coniferous forest

flat valley floor used for farming

Annotations are sentences which offer **explanation**.

steep sided V-shaped valley

interlocking spur

deciduous woods

erosion of debris from slope mass movement

Worked example

Look at the OS map extract of Warkworth and Amble. Mark the following onto the sketch map:

1 A tourist information feature **(1 mark)**

2 A water feature **(1 mark)**

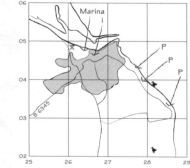

Ordnance Survey Maps, © Crown copyright 2016, OS 100030901 and supplied by courtesy of Maps International

Now try this

Explain **one** advantage of using annotated diagrams to explain the formation of a river meander. **(2 marks)**

119

Physical and human patterns

You may be asked to use photos, maps or sketches to describe or explain **physical** and **human** patterns. This skill is used throughout all the assessment elements in each component.

Describing patterns

You should learn to **describe** and/ or **explain** the **distribution** and **pattern** of **physical features** (rivers and coastlines) and **human features** (settlements and roads).

> Use the same technique you would use to describe any other type of pattern.

- You can use maps, photos and sketches to describe an area (e.g. rivers and coastlines).
- You can describe the site of a settlement using a map (e.g. settlements and roads).
- A photo or sketch can provide more detail about the **function** of the settlement.

> For more about atlas and map skills, see page 116.

Worked example

Describe the section of the River Browney and its valley shown on the map extract.
Use map evidence in your answer.

(3 marks)

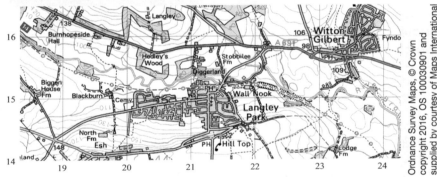

Ordnance Survey Maps, © Crown copyright 2016, OS 100030901 and supplied by courtesy of Maps International

> Make sure you use a good range of descriptive comments and map evidence.

This section of the River Browney shows the river moving from a V-shaped valley in the north-west of the map extract into a wider valley in the south-east. The V-shaped valley is only around 100 m wide at river level, with sides sloping up quite steeply to elevations of around 160 m. The river valley then widens to approximately 500 m, and is flat. There are a number of river meanders as the river valley widens, especially at grid reference 205153 and 233152.

Now try this

Suggest reasons why Settlement Y has grown.

(3 marks)

> Remember to focus on the **human** and **physical** reasons for the growth of the settlement.

1986	2016
X:1100 · Y:3800 → Y	X:740 · Y:7000
Z:16000 · N↑	Z:17200 · N↑

Key

▭ river	■ public house	+ church	● primary school	■ shop
▬ main road	▢ post office	∧ mountains	○ secondary school	X:1100 settlement and population size

Land use and settlement shapes

OS maps show **land use**, **vegetation types**, **communications** and the **shape** of settlements. You may be asked to describe these features.

OS map features

On an OS map you will find information about:

- land use (settlements and farmland)
- vegetation (woods and parklands)
- communications (roads and railways).

You may need to **describe** the **pattern** or **trend** shown on the map.

> The OS map key will help you identify different types of land use.

> For more about atlas and map skills, see page 116.

Describing settlements

To **describe** and **identify** settlements remember the 3 Ss:

- **site** – physical characteristics of the place
- **situation** – location in relation to other places
- **shape** – the way the settlement looks from an aerial view.

Remember also: **SAGA**
Slope (gentle or steep),
Aspect (north, east, south or west-facing),
Ground conditions (for example, floodplain),
Altitude (height above sea level).

Settlement shapes

There are three types of settlement shape.

Dispersed   Nucleated   Linear

Ordnance Survey Maps, © Crown copyright 2016, OS 100030901 and supplied by courtesy of Maps International

---

Worked example

Look at the OS map extract.

Find King's Caple in grid square 5628 and grid square 5629.

1 Put a cross in the correct box to describe the shape of King's Caple. **(1 mark)**
   - ☒ **A** nucleated
   - ☐ **B** scattered
   - ☐ **C** dispersed
   - ☐ **D** random

2 Explain your answer to question **1**. **(2 marks)**

The buildings are grouped around one area; therefore it is nucleated.

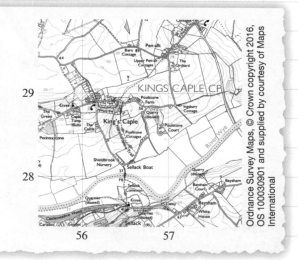

> When describing patterns you will need to give map evidence to do well. Use grid references, road or settlement names, distances and directions.

Now try this

Look at the map extract in the Worked example.

Describe the distribution of woodland shown on the map. Use map evidence in your answer. **(3 marks)**

Human activity and OS maps

You need to be able to recognise different types of human activity on an OS map. You may be tested on these.

OS maps may show evidence of different types of human activity.

Industrial (e.g. factories and industrial estates)

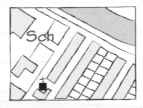

Residential (e.g. houses and flats)

Rural (e.g. forestry and agriculture)

Worked example

Look at the map extract of Ross-on-Wye.

Identify **two** pieces of map evidence that show non-residential activity by humans. **(2 marks)**

At 620228 there is a farm and at 586233 there is an industrial works.

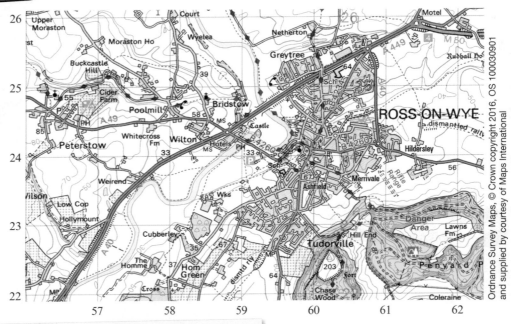

You need to name **two** different types of evidence you can see on the map. You can give a grid reference for each one, to show that you know where they are.

Now try this

Ross-on-Wye has a population of around 10 000 people. Use the OS map extract above to complete the table with **two** more community facilities and your sketched version of the symbol for each. An example has already been provided for you. **(2 marks)**

You need to include the **name** of the facility and the appropriate **symbol**.

Facility	Symbol
Car park	P

Map symbols and direction

Accurate use of OS maps requires important skills, such as using the **key** to identify **symbols**, and use of the compass to work out aspect or direction.

Map symbols

OS maps use symbols to represent features.

🦤 nature reserve
🏛 place of worship with tower
⋈ bridge
📞 public phone
🌳 non-coniferous trees

Take care! When answering questions on direction make sure you start from the correct feature!

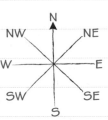

Compass points

You may be asked about the **direction** of features from each other.

You will need to learn the **eight** main compass points.

OS maps

This is a 1:50 000 extract from an OS map. This means that 1cm on the map represents 50 000 cm (500 m) in real life.

Look carefully at OS maps to spot the symbols and identify features.

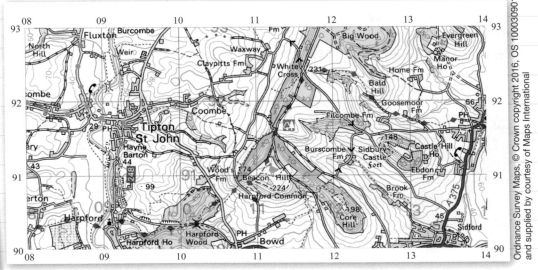

Ordnance Survey Maps, © Crown copyright 2016, OS 100030901 and supplied by courtesy of Maps International

---

Worked example

1 What do the following symbols mean on an OS map?   **(3 marks)**

PH public house (pub)

🌲🌲 coniferous trees

--- footpath

2 In the box below, draw the symbol for an embankment.   **(1 mark)**

Make sure you know what the symbol means by using the key on the OS map.
You do not need to memorise the symbols. Do not draw symbols too large and always use a **sharp pencil**.

Now try this

Look at the OS map extract above.
1 What symbol is found at 137913?   **(1 mark)**
2 Which direction is Bald Hill in 1292 from Ebdon Farm in 1391?   **(1 mark)**

Grid references and distances

Grid references are used to locate geographical features on an OS map. You need to know how to use grid references accurately.

Grid references

Each line on the map grid has a number. You can use these numbers to locate the features on a map.

You write the distance **along** (from the horizontal **easting** line) before the distance **up** (from the vertical **northing** line). For example, the shaded grid square has a 4-figure grid reference. To find this, you would go **along** the corridor, (13), then **up** the stairs, (02).

The telephone on this map has a 6-figure grid reference 138026.

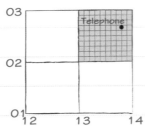

To write a 6-figure grid reference you have to mentally divide the edge of each grid square into 10 parts.

Measuring distance

You will need to work out **distances**. There are two types:

1 Distances from one point to another in a **linear** fashion are called **straight line** distances – sometimes called 'as the crow flies'.

2 Distances which follow a **curved** pattern, usually along a river or road, are called **winding** distances.

For the exam you will need a ruler to measure **straight line** distances and a 10-cm piece of string for **winding** distances.

The string should be provided for you if it is needed in the exam, but bring your own piece of string just in case.

Remember, you will be required to convert the distance measured using the ruler or string into kilometres (or metres if more appropriate) – use the scale line on the OS map to help you.

Worked example

Look at the OS map extract on page 123.

1 What is the name of the hill in grid square 1392? **(1 mark)**

Evergreen Hill

2 What is the 6-figure grid reference of the telephone in 1391? **(1 mark)**

137913

Watch out! A pointer line from the telephone symbol (grid square 1391) shows the **actual** position of the telephone on the main road.

Ordnance Survey Maps, © Crown copyright 2016, OS 100030901 and supplied by courtesy of Maps International

Now try this

Look at the OS map extract on page 123.

1 To the nearest kilometre, what is the straight line distance from Brook Farm in grid square 1290 to Home Farm in grid square 1392? **(1 mark)**

2 What type of woodland can be found in grid square 1192? **(1 mark)**

3 What is the 6-figure grid reference of the nature reserve near the centre of the map extract? **(1 mark)**

Cross sections and relief

A **cross section** is a visual representation of the **relief** (change in height) and features of a landscape along a **transect** – a specific straight line across the landscape. You may be asked to draw or label a cross section for a transect you have been given, or to comment on one.

Drawing a cross section

1 Place a strip of paper along the given transect line.

2 Mark off the points where the major (brown) contour lines meet the transect line.

3 Mark the location of other features such as rivers, roads or high points.

4 Draw a line on the grid paper to be the x-axis of your cross section. Line the strip of paper up with this x-axis.

5 Mark off the height of each contour line using a neat cross. Join up the crosses with a ruler and a sharp pencil.

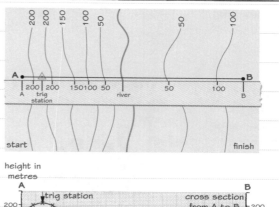

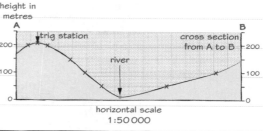

Slopes

The closer the contours, the steeper the slope!

There are different types of slope:
- **concave** slope.
- **convex** slope.

Worked example

Look at the map extract on the right.

Put a cross in the box below to describe the shape of the land from A to B.   **(1 mark)**

☐ **A** The land rises more gently towards the west.

☒ **B** The land at B is the highest.

☐ **C** The land at A is the highest.

☐ **D** The river goes through coniferous forest.

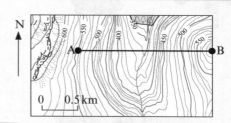

In multiple-choice questions look at the number of marks as this is likely to tell you the number of answers required.

Now try this

Look at the map extract in the Worked example.
Create a cross section of line A–B.   **(4 marks)**

Graphical skills 1

In your exam you may be asked about different types of graphs and charts: to interpret the data they provide and also possibly about when it is appropriate to use a particular chart or graph.

Line chart

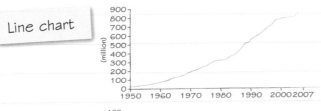

Line charts are used to plot continuous data. They are often used to show how something varies over time. Make sure you plot the points accurately and join the points with a continuous line.

Bar chart

Bar charts are used to plot discontinuous data. Make sure you draw bar charts with a ruler to keep the lines straight.

Pie chart

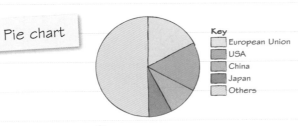

Key
- European Union
- USA
- China
- Japan
- Others

Pie charts show proportions. They are easy to read and fairly simple to put together. Data need to be converted into percentages first and then into proportions of 360° – the whole pie.

Scatter plot

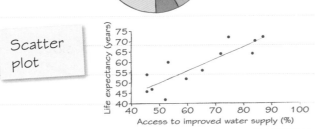

Scattergraphs show the relationship between two sets of figures. It is the pattern the points make that is important, so don't join up the points. If the line of best fit slopes downwards it is a negative correlation; if it is upwards it is a positive correlation. Some scattergraphs do not show any relationship.

Pictogram

300 000 hectares   200 000 hectares   100 000 hectares

Pictograms represent data using appropriate symbols that are drawn to scale. They present data in a very clear way. However, detailed information can get lost. A key explains the relationship between the data and the pictogram.

Histogram

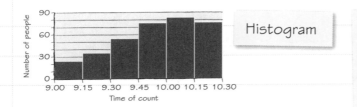

Histograms are used for continuous data. There are no gaps between the bars. The bars should be the same width for each category: this is called equal class intervals. The same colour is used for each bar because the data are continuous.

Now try this

What kind of chart or graph would you use to illustrate the following sets of data?

(a) Population growth in China from 1950 to 2010.   **(1 mark)**

(b) The relationship between the size of settlements and the number of services in each.   **(1 mark)**

(c) The proportion of people from different ethnic groups living in an inner city area.   **(1 mark)**

Graphical skills 2

You should also know how to interpret and extract information from triangular graphs, radial graphs, wind rose diagrams and proportional symbols.

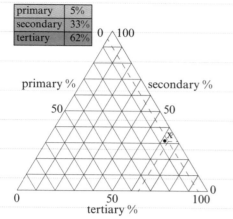

primary	5%
secondary	33%
tertiary	62%

Triangular graphs

A **triangular graph** has three axes, each divided up into percentages totalling 100. Three sets of data are needed (on the diagram these are primary, secondary and tertiary industry employment).

> To construct a triangular graph, lines are drawn at an angle of 60° (see the dotted lines). The plot (x) is made where these three lines meet.

Radial graphs, radar graphs and wind rose diagrams

A **radial graph** is used to plot one variable against a compass direction or time: for example, looking at where people come from to shop in a city centre. These graphs can also be used to plot bipolar data.

A **radar graph** is used to show multivariate data. It plots the values of each category along a separate axis, starting in the centre and ending on the outer ring.

A **wind rose diagram** shows the wind direction over a period of time. The length of the arm represents the frequency that the wind blows from each direction.

Radial graph showing wind direction

Radar graph showing data on levées

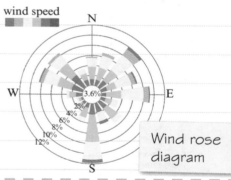

Wind rose diagram

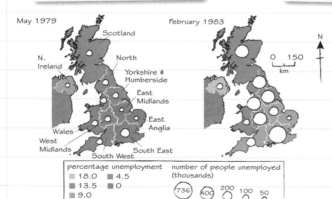

Proportional symbols

Proportional symbols can be plotted on maps with the size of the symbol (often a circle) proportional to the represented value. Proportional symbols can be hard to draw, as it is important to get the scale correct.

> On this map, proportional circles represent the regional distribution of unemployment in the UK during 1979 and 1983.

percentage unemployment	number of people unemployed (thousands)
18.0 4.5	
13.5 0	736 400 200 100 50
9.0	

Now try this

Study the proportional circles map above. Describe the changes in the number of people unemployed in the UK between 1979 and 1983.

(3 marks)

Graphical skills 3

You should also know how to interpret population pyramids, choropleth maps and flow-line maps.

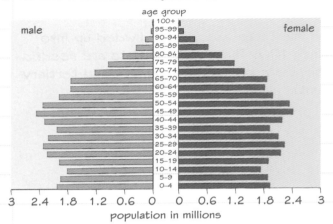

United Kingdom 2014

Population pyramids

Population pyramids are graphs that display data about the age structure of a population.

* The data are split into males and females.
* The data are presented in age groups.

Interpreting population pyramids

* Developing countries are often pyramid shapes: large numbers of children, lower life expectancy.
* Sides get straighter with development as birth rate reduces and life expectancy increases.
* Pyramids of ageing populations start to look top-heavy.

deciles of deprivation
10% most deprived
10% least deprived

Choropleth maps

Choropleth maps are shaded so that each type of shade represents a particular range of values. They are often constructed using base maps such as government administrative areas.

Choropleth maps are very good for showing how something varies over a geographical area. One problem is that they can suggest abrupt changes between areas where actual changes are much more gradual.

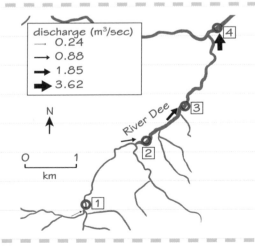

discharge (m³/sec)
— 0.24
→ 0.88
➔ 1.85
➡ 3.62

River Dee

N

0   1
km

Flow-line maps

Flow-line maps are drawn so that arrows show the direction of flows and the thickness of the arrows are proportional to the size of the flow.

Flow-line maps are easy to understand and give a clear indication of movement. The relative sizes of the flows can also be clearly seen. However, if lots of flows are going in the same direction the map can start to look very complicated.

Double-headed arrows can be used to show flows in two directions.

Now try this

Explain **one** advantage of using choropleth maps.   **(2 marks)**

Numerical and statistical skills 1

You will use your maths skills and statistics skills in specific ways for particular topics but these skills may also come up in any of the exam papers.

Some key maths and statistics terms

Proportion – when two values are in direct proportion, then as one increases, so does the other by the same percentage. If one decreases by the same percentage as the other increases, then this is called inverse proportion.

Magnitude – how big something is.

Frequency – how often something happens.

Quartiles – the values that divide a list of numbers into quarters.

Quintiles – the values that divide a list of numbers into fifths.

Percentiles – percentiles divide a list of numbers into percentages. If you are on the 60% percentile for height in your class, 60% are shorter than you.

Finding the percentage of an amount

To find the percentage of an amount:

1 divide the percentage by 100

2 multiply by the amount.

Example: 84% of the UK's population of 64 million people live in England.

$84 \div 100 = 0.84$

$0.84 \times 64 = 53.76$

So 53.76 million (53 760 000) people live in England.

One quantity as a percentage of another

To find one quantity as a percentage of another:

1 divide the first quantity by the second

2 multiple your answer by 100.

Example: A country's total energy production is 32 million tonnes of oil equivalent. 8 million tonnes comes from coal. As a percentage, this is:

$8 \div 32 = 0.25$

$0.25 \times 100 = 25$

So 25% comes from coal.

Percentage increase/decrease

To work out the percentage increase:

1 For increase, work out the difference between the two numbers like this:

new number – original number = increase

2 Then divide the increase by the original number and multiply the answer by 100.

To work out the percentage decrease, use:

original number – new number = decrease

Divide the decrease by the original number and multiply by 100.

Ratios

A ratio indicates the relationship between two quantities, usually in terms of how many times one goes into another. You can find equivalent ratios by multiplying or by dividing by the same number.

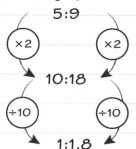

5:9
×2   ×2
10:18
÷10   ÷10
1:1.8

Here, the equivalent ratio takes the form 1:n. This can be useful in calculations.

Ratios can show risk or odds. For example, flood 1:200 maps show areas where there is a one in 200 chance (or more) of flooding each year.

Now try this

The population of Mumbai's metropolitan area has increased from 8 million in 1971 to 21 million in 2014. What is the percentage increase in Mumbai's population? **(1 mark)**

Numerical and statistical skills 2

Averages and other measures of central tendency help us manage sets of data by giving us a way of easily describing and comparing them. You need to know about median, mean, range, quartiles and interquartile range, mode and modal class.

Mode
The mode is the value that occurs **most often**.

> 4 5 9 7 4 4
> The mode of these six numbers is 4

Mean
To find the mean you add together all the numbers and then divide by how many numbers there are. Don't round your answer.

> 4 5 9 7 4 4
> The mean of these numbers is 5.5
> $4 + 5 + 9 + 7 + 4 + 4 = 33$
> $33 \div 6 = 5.5$

Median
The median is the **middle value**. First write the values in order from smallest to largest. If there are two middle values, the median is halfway between them.

> 4 4 4 5 7 9
> The median is 4.5

Range
The range is the largest value minus the smallest value.

> 4 5 9 7 4 4
> The range of these numbers is $9 - 4 = 5$

Modal class

When data are grouped, the modal class is the group that has the highest frequency.

The modal class of the data is the size group that comes up most frequently.

Study the table opposite to see how this works.

Modal class = 21–25 mm

Size of stones (mm)	Number of stones
1–5	5
6–10	11
11–15	7
16–20	5
21–25	13
26–30	9
31–35	2

Quartiles and interquartile range

The median is the middle value: the halfway split in the data. Quartiles divide each half of the data into half, giving us quarters.

The **lower quartile** is the value that divides the lower half of the data into two halves. The **upper quartile** divides the upper half of the data.

The **interquartile range** is the difference between the upper quartile and the lower quartile.

A formula for the median value is $(n + 1) \div 2$

A formula for the lower quartile is $(n + 1) \div 4$

A formula for the upper quartile is $3(n + 1) \div 4$

> 2 5 5 7 9 11 13

There are 7 numbers here, so the median value is $(7 + 1) \div 2 =$ the 4th value in the list: 7

The lower quartile is $(7 + 1) \div 4 =$ the 2nd value in the list: 5

The upper quartile is $3(7 + 1) \div 4 =$ the 6th value in the list: 11

Now try this

What is the interquartile range for the numbers:
2 5 5 7 9 11 13 ?   **(1 mark)**

ANSWERS

Where an example answer is given, this is not necessarily the only correct response. In most cases there is a range of responses that can gain full marks.

COMPONENT 1: THE PHYSICAL ENVIRONMENT

Changing UK landscapes

1. Main UK rock types
Igneous rocks are formed from cooling magma, but sedimentary rocks are formed from the deposition of materials. Igneous rocks do not contain fossils, whereas sedimentary rocks do.

2. Upland and lowland landscapes
The upland areas of Britain were formed through tectonic processes; intense pressure formed metamorphic rocks. Rising magma cooled and solidified to create igneous rocks such as granite.

3. Physical processes
B   Chalk

4. Human activity
The site for Shrewsbury was chosen because there is flat land surrounded by a river meander, which provided a good defensive position.

Coastal landscapes

5. Physical processes 1
Flat surfaces, such as bedding planes, will cause slides in which a large mass of material moves downhill. This will occur when the material has been subjected to extended periods of heavy rainfall, saturating the rock, making it heavier and more prone to slide.

6. Physical processes 2
Waves can transport material through a process called traction. This is where large boulders are rolled along the seabed by the waves. Another way waves can transport material is through suspension, where sand and particles move with the flow of the waves. *For 4 marks you must give at least two methods. You could also have mentioned saltation, where smaller stones are bounced along the sea bed; or solution, where some minerals are dissolved in sea water and carried along in the flow.*

7. Influence of geology
Headlands; bays

8. UK weather and climate
The UK's storms can result in erosion of coastal spits, which may be totally removed or realigned. *Other answers could include: removal of beach sediment; removal of sand dunes.*

9. Erosional landforms
Coastal stacks are formed at headlands where destructive waves attack lines of weakness, known as joints and faults. Over time, erosion processes of hydraulic action and abrasion increase the size of the joints and faults, causing caves to form. Continued erosion increases the size of the cave on narrow headlands, creating an arch. As the arch widens from continued erosion and weathering it eventually collapses, forming a column of rock, known as a stack.

10. Depositional landforms
Beaches are made up of sand, shingle and pebbles and are formed when deposition of transported material occurs over time. Waves lose energy as they approach land and therefore deposit material. The less powerful constructive waves are more important in beach formation, with the waves' swash moving more material up the beach than is being taken away by the backwash.

11. Human activity
Industry can affect coastal environments due to pollution. Oil refineries located near coastlines can lead to water pollution from spills and leaks during the production process, which can be harmful to aquatic life. A second impact of industry is the disruption to animal habitats during the construction of factories, causing species numbers to be reduced, leading to a reduction in biodiversity.

12. Coastal management
One advantage of using groynes is that they trap sediment, helping to broaden the beach, which helps to absorb wave energy. *Other advantages could include: groynes are a cheap form of coastal management.* A disadvantage of using groynes is that they prevent the process of longshore drift, which can have impacts further along the coastline, with increased erosion of cliffs.

13. Holderness coast
Use the case study that you have studied. Example: The coastal landscape at Dawlish Warren is made up of a spit that has changed in size, shape and position over time. Continued erosion over many years has caused the neck of the sand spit to become much narrower. Storms have caused strong destructive waves to erode the beach and sand dunes on the spit. This has meant that sea defences had to be installed, including 18 groynes to maintain the beach and gabions to protect the sand dunes. This has changed the landscape.

River landscapes

14. Physical processes 1
One process of mass movement is slumping. This happens when there is movement down the river valley sides along a plane such as a bedding plane. The material that moves is usually saturated due to intense rainfall. *Other answers could include: sliding.*

15. Physical processes 2
Hydraulic action is the force of the water hitting the riverbed and banks, causing them to be worn away, whereas attrition is when sediment particles transported by the river collide with each other, causing the particles to become rounder and smaller.

16. River valley changes
Your answer will depend on the river you have studied: e.g. The source of the River Holford is the Quantocks, Somerset and it flows for 7.8 km into the Bristol Channel at Kilve. The width of the river increases downstream because the upper course flows across impermeable hard sandstone, but in the lower course

it flows over a softer rock (marl), which is eroded more easily and therefore makes a wider channel. The bedload becomes much smaller and more rounded near the river mouth. This is because the resistant sandstone is difficult to erode and near the source there has been a short time for attrition. The soft marls erode rapidly so the bedload in the mid and lower course is small and rounded. The river discharge increases downstream as tributaries join the main river (e.g. at Hodder's Combe) and this increases the amount of water in the main river. There are small waterfalls in the upper course where the river flows over bands of very hard rock that are resistant to erosion. In the middle and lower course there are floodplains where the river has laterally eroded the softer marls.

17. Weather and climate challenges

1 2014
2 The increased rainfall during 2014 would lead to more water flowing into the river channel, creating a higher discharge.

18. Upper course landscape

Questions like this cover Assessment Objectives 3 and 4. For Assessment Objective 3, you need to apply your knowledge and make a judgement. For Assessment Objective 4, you need to choose and use the right skill to investigate the question, then put together a clear, well-balanced answer. In this case, you need to apply your knowledge of river processes and use your map skills to interpret what you see on the map. Remember to use evidence from the resource in your answer.

As this is an **examine** question, you need to break things down, then put together a clear, well-balanced answer, explaining how the elements interlink.

Example answer
Waterfalls on the map extract form in the upper courses of the rivers. This is shown by the narrow V-shaped river valleys where the contour lines are very close together. This indicates that vertical erosion, especially abrasion and hydraulic action, is taking place. The rivers with waterfalls flow from upland areas (over 230 metres) mostly in a south or south-west direction. The waterfalls occur when there is a sudden change in gradient in a river's course, shown by the contour lines. This may be because the geology of the area is hard, more resistant rock lying over the top of soft, less resistant rock. Over time, the river erodes the less resistant rock through processes like hydraulic action and abrasion, causing an overhang of the hard, more resistant rock. Continued erosion leads to the hard, more resistant rock being unable to support its own weight and collapsing due to gravity. The action of the water swirling the rocks around causes erosion of the large angular boulders, which over time, leads to the formation of a plunge pool.

19. Lower course landscape 1

When a river floods, water overflows the riverbanks on to the floodplain. As it does so, the river immediately loses velocity and energy and deposits the larger and heavier sediment first. Over time, repeated flooding and deposition cause these natural banks to get higher, forming levées.

20. Lower course landscape 2

Questions like this are looking for you to apply your knowledge and skills, using evidence from the resource in your answer (in this case, using your knowledge of the processes involved in forming a meander and your geographical skills to understand and use the detail on the diagram).

Example answer
The formation of a meander begins with the flow of the water being forced towards the banks of the river in a zigzag pattern. These areas of the banks receive maximum velocity. This causes lateral erosion, especially due to hydraulic action and abrasion, leading to undercutting. The undercut area eventually collapses under the force of gravity, creating a steep river cliff. A bend or meander starts to form. On the inside of the bend, the velocity and force of the water are less, which causes deposition of material. This creates a more gently sloping bank, which eventually forms a curving point bar. Over time, continued erosion on the outside of the bend and deposition on the inside of the bend will cause the meander to become larger and the river's course more sinuous.

21. Human activity

One of the human processes contributing towards flooding along the River Severn is building and urbanisation. There haven't been more settlements built, but an increase in settlement size. Towns, such as Shrewsbury and Bewdley, have larger areas of impermeable surfaces. These impermeable surfaces cause rapid surface run-off, meaning more water reaches the river channel at a faster rate, leading to flooding.

22. Causes and effects of flooding

1 12 – 6 = 6 hours

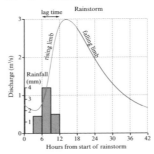

23. River management

Hard engineering methods are normally built defences using wood or concrete, such as channelisation, whereas soft engineering methods are a more natural approach to river management, such as using washlands. Soft engineering methods are usually cheaper, requiring little maintenance, whereas hard engineering methods are more expensive and often require regular maintenance to ensure their effectiveness.

24. River Dee, Wales

Questions like this cover Assessment Objectives 2 and 3. For Assessment Objective 2, you need to show that you understand the concepts involved (in this case, what the human and physical factors are). For Assessment Objective 3, you need to apply what you know to show how the processes, place and environment are linked and how they interact (in this case, how physical factors like climate and human factors like channelisation work together).

Example answer
The River Dee begins on the slopes of Dduallt in Snowdonia National Park, North Wales, and forms an estuary where it reaches the Irish Sea. A physical factor causing landscape change is variations in the UK climate. Due to global climate change, which is largely due to human factors, prolonged periods of heavy rainfall are increasing river levels and rates of erosion and deposition. This will cause landscape changes, e.g. higher levées. In the Dee Estuary a potential rise in sea level, also caused by global climate change, of 1 m by the year 2100, could result in flooding of salt and freshwater marshes, again altering the landscape.

Another human factor that has changed the natural course of the River Dee is the channelisation of 8 km of the river's course during the 1730s. The channel was straightened and this has increased both the discharge and velocity, increasing the risk of flooding to properties further downstream. Another human factor that has caused change to the landscape is the construction of a series of reservoirs like the Lynn Celyn under the RDRS (River Dee Regulation Scheme). This has increased storage of water, which has altered the course of the river by creating artificial wide, deep lakes.

Overall, a combination of physical and human factors working together have and will continue to cause change to the landscape surrounding the River Dee's course.

Glaciated upland landscapes

25. Glacial processes
Scree

26. Erosional landforms 1
Tarn (corrie lake)

27. Erosional landforms 2
A hanging valley is formed from the joining of a small tributary glacier and a larger glacier. The processes of plucking and abrasion deepen both glacial troughs, but the larger glacier creates a deeper and wider trough. Once the ice melts a large U-shaped trough is left by the larger glacier, whereas the smaller glacier valley is higher up the sides of the main trough and appears to be hanging.

28. Transport and depositional landforms
A crag and tail is formed when a glacier is forced to move over and around a band of hard, resistant rock. On the upstream side the slope is steepened and made jagged by plucking and abrasion, causing the crag to form. On the lee of the crag a tail is formed by deposition of glacial till, which decreases further away from the crag, resulting in the tail tapering off.

29. Human activity
The construction of hydro-electric power (HEP) stations and wind farms has caused disruption to wildlife habitats, leading to the loss of species, reducing biodiversity. A second impact is tourism. The rise in the number of tourists visiting these landscapes for walking holidays is causing footpath erosion and pollution of the landscape through littering.

30. Glacial development
Questions like this cover Assessment Objectives 2 and 3. For Assessment Objective 2, you need to show that you understand the concepts involved (in this case, what glaciated upland landscapes are like). For Assessment Objective 3, you need to apply what you know to show how the processes, place and environment are linked and how they interact (in this case, how people use these landscapes, and what impact this has).

As this is an **assess** question, you need to weigh up the factors against each other and decide which is the most important.

Example answer
One of the ways human activities have negatively changed glaciated upland landscapes is through quarrying. For example, in Snowdonia, a glaciated landscape, the closure of the slate quarries has left the landscape scarred by waste tips, derelict tramways and railways. The Dinorwig Power Station was built in a disused quarry to generate hydro-electric power (HEP), and its reservoir and dam have further altered the local landscape.

Glaciated upland landscapes are very popular tourist destinations. One of the key attractions for many is walking, but this has had a negative impact on the landscape. The volume of people walking up Snowdon each year has increased soil erosion of footpaths and led to the construction of engineered stone paths. Combined with the building of a visitor centre, this has spoiled the natural appearance of the local glaciated mountain landscape.

However, other human activities have had a more extensive impact. Large blocks of coniferous trees (for example, Coed y Brenin) have had a very significant effect on the appearance, ecosystems and drainage of glaciated landscapes.

Human activity has caused significant change to upland glaciated landscapes. To prevent further damage in the future glaciated landscapes like Snowdonia National Park will require careful management.

Weather and climate

31. Global atmospheric circulation
The atmospheric circulation transfers surplus heat energy from the equator to the polar regions by three circulation cells in each hemisphere. The largest cell is the Hadley cell where high-level winds transfer heat energy from the equator to 30 degrees north and south.

32. Natural climate change
A volcanic eruption can cause large volumes of ash and dust to be ejected into the atmosphere. This acts as a blanket over the Earth, causing temperatures to fall because the Sun's solar radiation is blocked out.

33. Human activity
Human activities can contribute to climate change through the increase in car ownership. This causes a rise in greenhouse gases, especially CO_2 released into the atmosphere from the exhaust fumes.

A second human activity is using new domestic technologies, which increases the demand for energy. This results in the increased burning of coal, oil and natural gas to generate electricity, which increases the amount of greenhouse gases being released into the atmosphere.

34. The UK's climate
The North Atlantic Drift brings warm water from the Gulf of Mexico northwards towards the UK. This causes the UK to have warmer than expected conditions for its latitude.

35. Tropical cyclones
Warm ocean temperatures of 27°C or more.

36. Tropical cyclone hazards
Category 5

37. Hurricane Sandy
Questions like this cover Assessment Objectives 2 and 3. For Assessment Objective 2, you need to show that you understand the concepts involved (in this case, what tropical cyclones are and the impacts they can have). For Assessment Objective 3, you need to apply what you know to show how the processes, place and environment are linked and how they interact (in this case, what sort of social and economic impacts a tropical cyclone can have on a developed country).

As this is an **evaluate** question, you need to review all the information, then bring it together, drawing on evidence such as relevant data, to make a supported judgement in your conclusion.

Example answer
Hurricane Sandy hit New Jersey, USA, on 29 October 2012 with wind speeds of 129 km/h and a powerful storm surge. One of the social impacts was that more than 150 people were killed, causing significant trauma to those who lost family members. This is the most significant social impact as the effects are long-lasting and affect many more people than the 150 killed. The hurricane also left over 4 million people in the states of New Jersey and New York without power. Rising flood waters and high winds caused considerable damage to schools, resulting in closures, so that many parents had to remain at home with their children. Although these two impacts are important they are short term and not as significant as the large number of people killed.

Economically, Hurricane Sandy caused an estimated US$65 billion worth of damage, which resulted in a considerable rise in the number of insurance claims made by individuals and businesses in New Jersey and New York. Estimated claims of over US$3 billion were made. This is important economically as it has both long-term and short-term implications. The large amount indicates the extent of the damage, and in the long term the cost of insurance in the affected area would have gone up, making the region more expensive to live in. The government was forced to pay for fuel to be imported due to a lack of supplies. Finally, the hurricane caused significant damage to many local businesses, with losses in New Jersey estimated at US$8.3 billion. This is the most important factor as many local businesses would have been destroyed, severely damaging the economy and employment.

In conclusion, Hurricane Sandy caused considerable social and economic impacts that have taken years to recover from.

38. Typhoon Haiyan

Questions like this cover Assessment Objectives 2 and 3. For Assessment Objective 2, you need to show that you understand the concepts involved (in this case, what tropical cyclones are and the impacts they can have). For Assessment Objective 3, you need to apply what you know to show how the processes, place and environment are linked and how they interact (in this case, what sort of social and environmental impacts a tropical cyclone can have on an emerging or developing country).

As this is an **evaluate** question, you need to review all the information, then bring it together, drawing on evidence such as relevant data, to make a supported judgement in your conclusion.

Example answer

Typhoon Haiyan hit the Philippines on 8 November 2013 with wind speeds of 306 km/h and a powerful storm surge, with tsunami-like waves reaching land at some 5 metres in height. One of the social impacts is that more than 6000 people were killed, with many more recorded missing. Alongside the trauma of family members losing relatives, homes were destroyed, with an estimated 4 million people initially displaced. This resulted in people without proper shelter, running water and food, and many people were still living in temporary shelters a year later. These are all very serious impacts, but the loss of life and the resulting trauma is the most significant.

Typhoon Haiyan caused a number of environmental impacts. These included damage to mangroves, which were already declining. If the mangroves had been established and protected before the typhoon, they would have acted as natural protection against the storm surge, and the impact might have been less severe. Therefore the additional damage to the mangroves is probably the most serious environmental impact.

Another environmental impact is the damage to an oil barge, which leaked 1.4 million litres of oil into the sea, resulting in damage to the aquatic ecosystem. The oil leak also released toxic benzene fumes into the atmosphere, which posed a threat to the lives of people living near the coastline. These are important but relatively localised impacts.

In conclusion, the typhoon that hit the Philippines had a number of significant social and environmental impacts that were unavoidable, but the depletion of mangroves years before the event could have increased the vulnerability of the country to the impacts of the storm surge.

39. Drought causes and locations

One meteorological cause of drought is when blocking anticyclones prevent low pressure systems and rain from reaching an area so that it receives less than average precipitation for a period of time.

40. California, USA

In California, people have responded to drought by raising awareness of the need for careful use of water. Campaigns such as 'Save our Water' educate citizens on how to use water more efficiently in the home. A second way people have responded to drought is that farmers are encouraged to use more water-efficient irrigation systems, like drip irrigation.

41. Ethiopia

One of the impacts of drought on ecosystems in Ethiopia is low water levels, causing a loss of habitats for fish and wildlife, for example the Borkena wetland.

Ecosystems

42. The world's ecosystems

Hot deserts like the Sahara in Africa are warm all year round, with extreme heat during the daytime and little rainfall, making the climate very dry.

43. Importance of the biosphere

Food resources – fish and meat; fuel resources – wood from trees and shrubs

44. The UK's main ecosystems

One reason marine ecosystems are important is that they provide income to the local economy through tourism, with millions of people visiting the UK coastlines every year. A second reason is because they create employment through commercial fishing.

45. Tropical rainforest features

Biotic characteristics are living elements of an ecosystem, like animals, whereas abiotic characteristics are non-living elements of an ecosystem, like soil.

46. TRF biodiversity and adaptations

One reason is that tropical rainforest has a complex, layered structure, which creates a range of different wildlife habitats. Each of these habitats can support different species, which creates a high level of biodiversity in the rainforest as a whole. *Other answers could include: hot, wet climate; long hours of sunlight and warm temperatures.*

47. TRF goods and services

One service provided by tropical rainforests is a home for indigenous people. *Other answers could include: TRF acting as a carbon store; source of revenue from tourism.*

48. Deforestation in tropical rainforests

One reason for deforestation is the growth in palm oil plantations, with palm oil becoming more important as a biofuel, as well as being used in cosmetics. Another reason is that in many areas rainforests are being cleared due to rising demands for minerals like iron ore.

49. Tropical rainforest management

One reason why tropical rainforests require sustainable management is that they provide a home for a diverse range of plant and animal species, like the Amazon rainforest with over 1300 bird species. Damage to these ecosystems can lead to a reduction in species numbers and potential extinction, so it is important to manage this for the future. *Other answers could include: provides resources (food, water, timber, medicines) for people locally and worldwide.*

50. Deciduous woodlands features

One characteristic of deciduous woodlands is fertile, brown-earth soils formed from leaf fall. *Other answers could include: slower leaching than in TRF; plants in herb layer blossom before larger plants grow leaves; bogs and ponds habitats.*

51. Deciduous woodlands adaptations

One way squirrels have adapted is through storing food, such as acorns from deciduous trees, by burying it to use in the winter. *Other answers could include: birds migrate away from the UK in winter; some animals hibernate.*

52. Deciduous woodlands goods and services

One of the ways climate change is a threat to deciduous woodlands is by potentially reducing the levels of biodiversity. This is caused by a rise in diseases threatening some species, due to the survival of pests during milder winters. Climate change could also cause significant changes to the structure of deciduous woodlands. This is because rising temperatures and drier conditions are making conditions more suitable for coniferous trees.

53. Deforestation in deciduous woodlands

One of the causes of deforestation in deciduous woodlands is the demand for new homes as a result of the rising UK population, resulting in large areas being cleared. Another cause is rising car ownership, which is leading to the removal of trees to enable the widening of roads. *Other answers could include: replanting with conifers; pesticide damage; need for farmland.*

54. Deciduous woodlands management

Questions like this cover Assessment Objectives 2 and 3. For Assessment Objective 2, you need to show that you understand the concepts involved (in this case, the characteristics of deciduous woodlands and tropical rainforest, and what sustainable management is). For Assessment Objective 3, you need to apply what you know to show how the processes, place and environment are linked and how they interact (in this case, how sustainable management relates to tropical rainforests and deciduous woodlands, and what the impact of this could be in the future).

As this is an **assess** question, you need to weigh up the factors against each other and decide which is the most important.

Example answer

Sustainability can be defined as 'meeting the needs of the present without compromising the ability of future generations to meet their own needs'. Sustainable management of tropical rainforests and deciduous woodlands means policies and practices should work to ensure that these areas are effectively conserved for today and for use by people in the future.

One of the ways the tropical rainforest has been managed is through educating farmers. The Association Mitsinjo suggests alternatives to widespread felling for agriculture by the more sustainable System of Rice Intensification (SRI), which reduces the amount of land cleared and increases the amount of food produced. Similarly, in the New Forest landowners are being provided with grants to improve levels of biodiversity by removing invasive species, planting native species, clearing undergrowth and adopting traditional sustainable techniques, such as coppicing. Such approaches allow the use of these areas in a controlled way that is essential for their future existence.

Tourism has increased in recent years, putting more pressure on fragile forest and woodland ecosystems. One of the strategies used to manage tourism more sustainably in Madagascar is eco-tourism. Association Mitsinjo works with local wildlife guides to escort tourists around the Analamazaotra Reserve in Madagascar, with the income obtained used to develop further sustainable practices.

In the New Forest, placing restrictions on where people can go reduces the damage caused by walkers, cyclists and car owners. For example, new car parks have been created to stop people from parking on roadside verges, and designated footpath and cycle routes ensure vulnerable areas are protected. This allows the use of the National Park but in a sustainable manner that is essential for its future.

In conclusion, in highly protected areas such as the New Forest, successful sustainable management is ensuring that the area can be used for recreation, farming and forestry, both now and in the future. However, although sustainable management is also essential for the future of rainforests, the policies presently being used are often unregulated and too small-scale to ensure their long-term existence.

Extended writing questions

55. Paper 1

Here is an example of how you could plan your answer.

Introduction
- Define deciduous woodlands and sustainability.

Middle
- Decide on the key words you will use in your answer, which will depend on the deciduous woodland you have studied in class.
- Choose two or three examples to illustrate the reasons why approaches are needed to manage deciduous woodlands.
- Remember to include specific points, such as key facts and figures.

Conclusion
- Make a decision about the validity of the statement – are different approaches needed to ensure successful management of deciduous woodlands?

COMPONENT 2: THE HUMAN ENVIRONMENT
Changing cities

56. An urban world

One of the factors that has caused variations in urbanisation rates is wealth, which has enabled developed countries to invest in industry and infrastructure at a much faster rate than developing countries.

57. UK urbanisation differences

There is a clear relationship between population distribution and the main urban centres. For example, high population density is found in the south-east, where the city of London is located. In the north, in the Scottish Highlands, population density is low, at 0–25 people per square kilometre, and there are no major urban centres located in this area.

58. Context and structure

Birmingham began on a south-facing sandstone ridge which is a dry point site. It is located on the Birmingham plateau in the Midlands region. Its situation in the centre of England includes excellent communications, e.g. to the city of Lichfield in Staffordshire to the north and the industrial city of Coventry to the east.

59. A changing UK city

One of the impacts of international migration is a shortage of housing, with UK cities like Birmingham struggling to meet the growing demand. A second impact is increased pressure on services such as GP surgeries and nursing care, which find it increasingly difficult to provide adequate services.

60. Globalisation and economic change

One of the causes of deindustrialisation in UK cities is globalisation, which has resulted in many large businesses moving their operations to other countries where production is cheaper, leading to the closure of factories in the UK. A second cause is developments in technology, which have resulted in the closure of smaller, less efficient companies that haven't been able to invest in new production methods.

61. City inequalities

The most deprived 5% of SOAs are mainly located in the central regions in Birmingham, like Washwood Heath and Bordesley Green. The most deprived 10% and 25% areas are scattered around Birmingham, but with a larger cluster located in the west at Stockland Green, Stechford and Yardley North.

62. Retailing changes

Internet shopping has caused the number of people who visit the shops to reduce, which can lead to the closure of smaller businesses.

63. City living

In Birmingham the city council has invested in developing energy-efficient housing to help its residents reduce their energy bills. The council has set up plans to improve insulation through new double-glazed windows and improved heating systems.

64. Context and structure

Mexico City's first site was an island in Lake Texcoco and it is now located on a flat upland landscape called the Central Plateau, surrounded by mountains and volcanoes. Its upland situation makes it a natural crossroads for trade between the arid north, the Gulf of Mexico to the east and the Pacific Ocean to the west.

65. A rapidly growing city

From 1950 to 2010 there has been a continual rise in the number of people living in the suburbs of Mexico City, growing from about half a million to about 17 million over 60 years. In contrast, the urban core population experienced a period of increase from 1950 to 1970, then started to decrease, and then levelled out from the year 2000.

66. Increasing inequalities

A squatter settlement is an area where people have settled illegally, building homes from a variety of scrap materials.

67. Solving city problems

Questions like this cover Assessment Objectives 2 and 3. For Assessment Objective 2, you need to show that you understand the concepts involved (in this case, what a major city in an emerging or developing country is like, and what sorts of development projects there are to improve life there). For Assessment Objective 3, you need to apply what you know to show how the processes, place and environment are linked and how they interact (in this case, the issues involved, the pros and cons of different types of development, and how different groups in the city are affected).

As this is an **evaluate** question, you need to review all the information, then bring it together, drawing on evidence such as relevant data, to make a supported judgement in your conclusion.

Example answer

To improve the lives of people living in cities, governments and NGOs use top-down and bottom-up development projects. Top-down development projects are normally funded and managed by the city government or a TNC, while bottom-up development projects are smaller-scale projects funded by NGOs and communities.

In Mexico City, the government has invested in sustainable transport schemes to improve air pollution and commuting. One of the schemes that has been introduced is the Metrobus, which can move 250 000 people around the city every day, reducing journey times by approximately 30 minutes. This benefits day-to-day commuting for Mexico City's residents. The scheme is also expected to reduce air pollution by 35 000 tonnes of CO_2 emissions each year. This is significant as it will have long-term health benefits.

A second scheme introduced by the government in 2011 was the garbage trading system. The disposal of waste is a major issue, with landfill sites becoming toxic grounds and a danger for its citizens. The closure of one of the landfill sites and the failure to find an alternative led to the introduction of trading rubbish for food. This involved setting up a 'barter market' with people exchanging waste for vouchers, which were then traded with local farmers for food. This project not only helped to deal with the waste disposal issue but also improved lives through increased access to food.

A number of bottom-up projects have been implemented. One example is Cultiva Ciudad, which is working with local schools to educate children about how to manage a garden, creating rooftop gardens to provide fresh, healthy food. This has helped to raise awareness of eating healthily and has provided learning opportunities for children, improving the lives of some of the poorer children.

In conclusion, Mexico City is a good example of how the combination of bottom-up and top-down projects can be valuable in helping to improve the lives of its people. The most successful project is the introduction of sustainable transport as this affects the largest number of people, but the other projects are important locally in improving the diet of some of the poorest people.

Global development

68. Defining development

One of the factors contributing to human development is access to education, represented as the literacy rate. This will improve people's lives by increasing their prospects of getting better-paid jobs. *Other answers could include: economic; social; technological; food and water security; and cultural factors.*

69. Measuring development

GDP per capita is the total value of goods and services produced by a country in a year divided by the population of that country.

70. Patterns of development

The pattern of GDP per capita in the UK varies, with the south and London having the highest rates, between £19 200 and £21 446. Lower rates of GDP per capita are found in the west of central England, Wales, Yorkshire and the Humber, and the North East.

71. Uneven development

Uneven development means universal primary education is a major problem in many developing countries. In Africa, more than 60% of secondary school-aged children do not attend school.

72. International strategies

International aid can help reduce uneven global development by voluntarily transferring resources from developed countries to developing countries. This helps to support the accumulation of enough capital to invest in industry and infrastructure. *Other answers could include: pay for imports; address a shortage of skills.*

73. Top-down vs bottom-up

Top-down development projects can lead to increased debt for the receiving country, because large sums may be required to fund a project. Debt reduces the possibility of further development. A second problem of top-down projects is that TNCs may take advantage of the local workforce, offering few jobs, often in low-paid positions and with poor working conditions. This stops them breaking out of the poverty cycle and prevents a reduction in uneven global development.

74. Location and context

Example answer: India's culture consists of different ethnic groups and religions. India has the third largest Muslim population in the world and 80% of the population are Hindus. People are grouped into 'castes', which are social ranks based on their parents' status.

75. Uneven development and change

One change in India's primary sector has been that the contribution of agriculture to India's GDP has fallen from 58% to 26%. This has had the impact of increased rural to urban migration, as more people move to cities in search of work. A change in India's quaternary sector has been the growth of one of the world's fastest-growing telecom markets, which has created over 1 million new jobs in the ICT industry.

76. Trade, aid and investment

The thicker trade flow arrows from India, indicating a higher number of exports, are in a west or north-west direction to the USA and the UK. India exports less to countries to the east and north-east (for example China), as is shown by the thinner arrows.

77. Changing population

One of the key changing social factors in India is improvements in education. The Indian government has invested in education by building more schools and encouraging investment in the private sector. This means that literacy rates for both men and women are rising, improving people's chances of getting jobs and better wages, especially those from lower social groups.

A second changing social factor is a reduction in gender inequality, with more opportunities for women to earn an income, e.g. through the entrepreneurship programme, where women are trained and then pass on their knowledge to other women. This has increased the status of women in the workplace and given them greater opportunities to make a living outside the home.

78. Geopolitics and technology

Example answer: Most of the technological advances made in India have been made in the southern part of India, especially within the 'golden triangle' of IT and technology, which consists of Hyderabad, Bangalore and Chennai. This means that states such as Bangalore in the south receive money from investment in technology and major IT companies have located in these areas, increasing investment, wages and development. In contrast, many of the more northern areas of India, such as Uttar Pradesh, have not attracted technology and remain largely subsistence agricultural areas with lower levels of investment, wages and development.

79. Impact of rapid development

Example answer: One of the impacts of rapid development on India is the pollution of water sources from waste disposal. Population increase and industrial development put pressure on waste disposal infrastructure but only 30% of the sewage is treated. The National Water Policy (2012) encourages recycling and reuse of water after treatment to remove pollutants. This policy is designed to improve the quality of life by reducing pollution of rivers and lakes, which leads to the spread of diseases. In addition, the government has set up the National Water Quality Monitoring Network to investigate water quality so that the areas and people most affected by poor water quality receive help.

Resource management

80. The world's natural resources

Renewable energy resources are potentially inexhaustible and can be replenished naturally, such as solar energy, whereas non-renewable energy resources are combustible sources and cannot be 'remade': for example, coal.

81. Variety and distribution

The map shows that the largest area of hill sheep farming is located in the north in the Scottish Highlands, with other key locations including Wales in the west of the UK and the north-west and Yorkshire. There is a small-scale scattered distribution of hill sheep farming in the south-west.

82. Global usage and consumption

B   100–200

Energy

83. Production and development

One advantage of developing wind energy is that it doesn't pollute the atmosphere with harmful greenhouse gases, which helps to limit global climate change.

84. UK and global energy mix

One of the factors that cause global variations in the energy mix is wealth. More developed countries have money available to invest in the construction costs of building wind and solar farms and hydro-electric power plants. *Other answers could include: availability; population.*

85. Impacts of non-renewable energy resources

One negative impact of developing a non-renewable energy resource such as oil is the potential for spills to occur. This can lead to pollution of ground- and drinking-water sources and damage to marine ecosystems. *Other answers could include: loss of farmland; large amounts of CO_2 produced (coal); pollution from storage (uranium).*

86. Impacts of renewable energy resources

One of the negative impacts on the environment of developing hydro-electric power is the removal of vegetation and forests to locate the dam. This results in a loss of natural vegetation and destruction of wildlife habitats, causing a decrease in species numbers and damage to the ecosystem.

Developing solar energy involves the construction of the solar panels. Each solar panel is built using toxic metals including cadmium, which can pollute the environment and affect the reproduction of soil micro-organisms.

87. Meeting energy demands

Many individuals, especially in developed countries, are becoming more aware of the need to manage domestic energy in the home in a sustainable way and to reduce their carbon footprint. Some people are making their energy consumption more sustainable by reducing the loss of heat energy by installing cavity wall insulation and double-glazed windows. However, people living near proposed wind farm sites have concerns about noise and visual impact and may oppose such sustainable developments.

88. China and Germany

Questions like this cover Assessment Objectives 2 and 3. For Assessment Objective 2, you need to show that you understand the concepts involved (in this case, what energy resources, sustainability and different levels of development are). For Assessment Objective 3, you need to apply what you know to show how the processes, place and environment are linked and how they interact (in this case, how successful different approaches are in two countries with different levels of development and different resources).

As this is an **assess** question, you need to weigh up the factors against each other and decide which is the most important.

Example answer

China is a developing country that is carrying out rapid industrialisation. In 2014, China was responsible for 29% of global carbon emissions. One of the strategies used to manage its energy resources more sustainably is the introduction of the China Renewable Energy Law in 2006, with the aim of developing further renewable energy resources to reduce its reliance on non-renewable resources. The government estimates that, through increased development of renewable resources, reliance on coal will reduce from 64% in 2015 to 58% in 2020. This policy has been a significant success. In 2013, China was the world's largest producer of renewable energy, with a total capacity of 378 GW, mainly wind and hydro-electric power. The Three Gorges Dam generates 98 billion kilowatt-hours of electricity, potentially saving 100 million tonnes of CO_2 emissions. While the project has proved its success in sustainable energy production, its construction resulted in damage to the biodiversity in the Yangtze.

Germany, a developed country, is a leading solar energy producer and has a number of large solar farms such as the Bavaria Solarpark, expected to produce an estimated 215 million kWh of clean energy over the next 20 years. It is part of the successful scheme, which means that the use of sustainable energy in Germany has increased from just over 6% in 2000 to 28% in 2014.

The German government has invested in replacing old wind turbines with new, more efficient designs to increase energy production. New wind farms are planned for offshore locations to increase sustainable energy output. Germany plans to increase its use of renewable energy to 30% by 2030.

China and Germany demonstrate how investment in new technologies can have a significant benefit on the reduction of CO_2 emissions and production of more clean energy, despite being at different stages of economic development.

Water

89. Global distribution of water

Areas of water scarcity tend to follow a linear pattern between the equator and the Tropic of Cancer, such as in the Sahara region of Africa. There are more isolated areas on the East African coast and clustered in the Middle East.

90. Changing water use

One of the reasons why the global demand for water has changed is rising affluence, which means more people can afford labour-saving devices such as washing machines and dishwashers. A second reason is more leisure time. This has increased demand for recreational facilities that use water, like water parks, spas and golf courses.

91. Water consumption differences

One of the key reasons for differences in water usage is the lack of piped water to homes in developing countries; therefore women and children are forced to walk long distances to collect water from wells or communal taps. This means that relatively little water is used, whereas in developed countries most homes have a piped water supply and this availability increases water use. Another reason for the differences is manufacturing. In many developed countries industrial processes involve the use of millions of litres of water every day in large-scale factory units, whereas in many developing countries less water is used in smaller-scale cottage industries. Another reason for the differences is agriculture: developed countries generally have sophisticated irrigation systems which use only the required amount of water, whereas in developing countries water is wasted by ineffective irrigation systems.

92. Water supply problems: UK

One of the reasons for the serious water supply problems in the south and south-east of the UK is a higher population density. London is located in this area and therefore the demand for water is much higher than in other areas but the annual rainfall levels tend to be lower. This creates a water deficit during certain times of the year.

93. Water supply problems: emerging or developing countries

Watercourses in developing countries may become polluted through the disposal of untreated sewage in streams, lakes and ponds. This can cause water-related diseases like cholera and typhoid. A second way watercourses can become polluted is through poor farming practices, allowing the unregulated use of fertilisers and pesticides which degrade water supplies and damage ecosystems. *Other answers may include: mining leading to health problems.*

94. Attitudes and technology

The exploitation and consumption of water can lead to disputes between stakeholders. Environmentalists believe the use of water should be carefully managed to prevent damage to groundwater supplies as well as river and lake ecosystems. However, many users such as golf course managers, who use water for irrigation, would prefer to have unlimited use. Many individuals in developed countries have installed low-flush toilets and aerators into shower heads to reduce the amount of water used by domestic activities. Other individuals, however, do not share the wish to conserve water and want grass lawns and swimming pools in water-deficit areas.

95. Managing water

Many large-scale businesses support the increased use of water. For example, in Las Vegas the tourist industry believes that freely available water is vital to maintain the number of visitors. This is not a sustainable view as Las Vegas is in a water-deficit area. Farmers in Las Vegas oppose excessive use of water for tourism and want water management, which allows a greater share of water for irrigating their crops. Environmentalists oppose the overuse of groundwater supplies and want strict management policies to protect fragile ecosystems.

96. UK and China

Questions like this cover Assessment Objectives 2 and 3. For Assessment Objective 2, you need to show that you understand the concepts involved (in this case, what water resources, sustainability and different levels of development are). For Assessment Objective 3, you need to apply what you know to show how the processes, place and environment are linked and how they interact (in this case, how successful different approaches are in two countries with different levels of development and different resources).

As this is an **assess** question, you need to weigh up the factors against each other and decide which is the most important.

Example answer

China is a developing country whose rapid economic growth has put increasing pressure on there being sufficient water supplies to meet the domestic and industrial demands. One of the strategies used to manage water more sustainably for agriculture is to make farming methods more efficient. Farmers are encouraged to use drought-resistant crop types and monitor rice fields so that water is only added when the soil monitor indicates a low moisture level. At present this has some success on larger farms, but many farms in more remote areas do not use these techniques. The government has invested in wastewater recycling plants; 22% of Beijing's total annual water use was supplied from recycled water in 2008. This is a relatively successful approach to managing water resources on a local scale. However, overall China only reclaims about 9% of wastewater compared to 70% by most developed countries, indicating that further investment is needed to improve national water management.

The UK is a developed country with water shortages in the south where the population density is highest. One of the strategies used to manage water more sustainably is through educating people about how to save water in the home. Many of the major water companies have produced leaflets and guidance on their websites encouraging people to manage their water use through, for example, replacing worn washers to stop dripping taps and installing water butts to water plants during the summer. However, such policies have limited success as industry uses 75% of the UK's water, so incentives to reduce industrial consumption are essential to an overall reduction in water usage.

Overall, the strategies used by China and UK demonstrate clear steps towards achieving sustainable use of water but increasing populations and demand mean additional policies are essential.

Extended writing questions

97. Paper 2

Your answer to either of these questions will depend on the case study you have studied in class. Use the following guide to check your answer.

Section A: Changing cities

- Define **urbanisation** at the start – urbanisation is the increase in the number of people living in urban areas compared to rural areas.
- Check that you have included two or three examples to evaluate which of the cities have been most successful in dealing with the impacts. These examples should have case study-specific facts to support your points. For example, if one of your cities was Mexico City you could talk about the new Metrobus, which has been set up for the benefit of both people and the environment. A specific fact you could mention in your answer is the estimated reduction of 35 000 tonnes of CO_2 emissions every year.
- Check that you have talked about the success for **both** people and the environment.
- Check that you have reached a conclusion, deciding which city has been more successful. You could finish your answer with the following sentence starter:
  To conclude, I think that …

Section B: Global development

- Define **geopolitical** at the start – geopolitical refers to the power and relationships a country has with other countries.
- Check that you have included two or three examples so that you can assess the effects these relationships have on your chosen emerging or developing country. These examples should have case study-specific facts to support your points. For example, if your chosen country was India you could talk about the effect of the competition for water resources India has with China. A specific point would be the conflict over the water resources on the Yarlung Tsangpo–Brahmaputra River.
- Remember you can talk about different types of relationship – foreign policy, defence, military pacts and territorial disputes. Check that you have talked about at least two different types of relationship in your answer.
- Check that you have reached a conclusion, identifying which relationship you think is having the deepest effects on your chosen country. You could finish your answer with the following sentence starter:
  To conclude, I think that …

COMPONENT 3: GEOGRAPHICAL INVESTIGATIONS

Fieldwork: coasts

98. Formulating enquiry questions

$3.0 + 2.8 + 3.9 + 2.0 + 1.0 + 2.6 = 15.3 \div 6 = 2.6$ (to 1 decimal place)

Remember: when calculating the mean you need to add all the numbers together and then divide by the number of variables.

99. Methods and secondary data

Measuring beach gradient = quantitative; using a questionnaire = qualitative

100. Working with data

The scattergraph shows that as the height of the beach increases, the size of the sediments decreases. For example, when the height of the beach is 8 mm/m the sediment size is 250 grams whereas when the height of the beach is 2 mm/m the sediment size is 1050 grams. There is an anomaly where the largest sediment size is found with a beach height of 5 mm/m.

Fieldwork: rivers

101. Formulating enquiry questions

$0.16 + 0.41 + 0.38 + 0.05 + 0.08 + 0.51 = 1.59 \div 6 = 0.27$ (to 2 decimal places)

Remember: when calculating the mean you need to add all the numbers together and then divide by the number of variables.

102. Methods and secondary data

Measuring the depth of the river = quantitative; using a questionnaire = qualitative

103. Working with data

The graph shows that the width of the river increases in the middle section of the sites surveyed, with a significant increase at site 6, a width of 4.1 m. This site is an anomaly. The width returns to a similar measurement, 1.25 m, at site 10 as sites 1 and 2.

Fieldwork: urban

104. Formulating enquiry questions

The answer to this question will depend on your own fieldwork location. Some points to think about are access, safety and sampling.

105. Methods and secondary data

The answer to this question will depend on your own fieldwork location. Answers should include an explanation of one advantage and one disadvantage of each fieldwork technique listed.

106. Working with data

The answer to this question will depend on your own fieldwork location and the type of sampling strategy you selected.

Fieldwork: rural

107. Formulating enquiry questions

The answer to this question will depend on your own fieldwork location. You will probably mention tallying the number of people passing you at a named location for a given period of time.

108. Methods and secondary data

The answer to this question will depend on your own fieldwork location. Answers should include an explanation of one advantage and one disadvantage of each fieldwork technique listed.

109. Working with data

The answer to this question will depend on your own fieldwork location. You must make clear reference to the sampling strategy you used, such as systematic sampling.

UK challenges

110. Consumption and environmental challenges

Building of houses on greenfield sites leads to the destruction of wildlife habitats and reduction in the biodiversity of the local environment. *Other answers could include: food demands; rise in CO_2; pressure on water systems; new houses potentially increasing flooding.*

111. Population and economic challenges

$340 - (-40) = 380$ thousand
When calculating the range you should identify the highest and lowest values and subtract the smallest value from the largest value.

112. Landscape challenges

Flood management in the UK is carried out using either soft or hard engineering techniques. Floodplain zoning is a soft engineering technique that is used to allocate areas of land to different uses on the basis of their flood risk potential: for example, housing is built on the areas least likely to flood. Another approach is land use management such as afforestation, which is the planting of trees to increase the rate of interception and reduce surface and groundwater flow. This reduces the amount of water entering the river and therefore the flood risk. *Other answers could include: monitoring systems; educating local residents; new regulations for building.*

113. Climate change challenges

One possible impact of future climate change is rising sea levels, which will lead to increased coastal flooding events, leading to higher rates of coastal erosion. *Other answers could include: heatwaves and droughts.*

Extended writing questions

114. Paper 3 (i)

The answer to this will depend on your chosen fieldwork location and the methods you used. For the coastal landscape study, you will have investigated coastal processes through landscape evidence.

Remember: for this question you will need to make an overall judgement on the effectiveness of your data collection methods.

When talking about the reliability of your chosen methods you will need to consider if there were any equipment errors, operator errors or issues with the chosen sampling method. For example, when collecting beach sediment, if a hand-grab sample was taken it might be that more than one person collected the sample in your group. This might have affected the size of the sample because it is subjective how the sample is grabbed and the sizes of people's hands are different.

You will need to show evidence in your answer that is related to your own fieldwork investigation. Try to talk about the location (sites) where your data collection methods were used, the sampling method used and the time of day you conducted the investigation.

115. Paper 3 (ii)

Here is an example of how you could improve the student answer with an introduction, a detailed middle section and a conclusion.

In order to discuss the view, it is important to define the two key terms: brownfield sites and greenfield sites. A brownfield site is an area of disused or derelict land that has been previously occupied by industry, whereas a greenfield site is an area that has not been previously built on – usually agricultural land.

There are a number of advantages and disadvantages to building on the two different sites and I will now discuss these. For brownfield sites, one of the key advantages is improving the aesthetics of the local environment by removing or renovating a previously derelict building or site. Derelict buildings can encourage crime as well as spoiling the landscape with broken windows and graffiti. Removing or renovating them can help to improve both the look of the area as well as helping to boost the local economy with increased opportunities for wider investment. For example, in Northwich, Cheshire, old unused Tata Steel chemical units have been demolished and replaced with new housing.

In comparison, building on a greenfield site can often ruin the look of the natural landscape, which can lead to protests to stop the projects obtaining planning permission. This is because building on greenfield sites not only spoils the landscape view for many local residents, but also leads to increased traffic congestion, which increases air and noise pollution. This increased pollution can also have significant impacts on wildlife.

A second key advantage of building on brownfield sites is that all the utilities like gas, electricity and water are already installed, which can reduce construction costs, whereas for greenfield sites these have to be installed, which can cause issues with increased roadworks and disruption to commuters. One disadvantage is that, while the utilities are in place on brownfield sites, the previous industry may have left hazardous waste that has to be cleared before renovation of the site can take place. The clearing of this hazardous waste can be expensive and potentially dangerous to locals, something that is not an issue with building on greenfield sites. This can result in increased costs and timescales for renovation of the brownfield site, which can often result in developers not being keen to take on the project, leaving brownfield sites derelict for longer periods of time.

In conclusion, there are many advantages and disadvantages associated with the use of brownfield sites and greenfield sites. The use of these sites will often depend on the local council and the planning regulations in place. It is clearly more beneficial to use brownfield sites: while they are slightly more expensive and could take time to renovate, they are not using up new land. This is therefore helping to improve the look of the local area, removing any potential hazards and not using up our natural countryside.

SKILLS

116. Atlas and map skills

Tropical rainforests are located both north and south of the equator between the Tropic of Capricorn and the Tropic of Cancer. The forests tend to follow a linear trend and are found in north-east South America, Central Africa and Asia.

117. Types of map and scale

(i) 062534 (ii) 065534

118. Using and interpreting images

One of the advantages of using oblique instead of vertical aerial photography is that the variations in the height of the landscape can be seen more easily. *Other answers could include: features are easier to identify.*

119. Sketch maps and annotations

Annotated diagrams provide good visual representations and explanations of the processes and stages involved in meander formation.

120. Physical and human patterns

Settlement Y is located at a crossroads, so access is easy, which would encourage nucleated settlements to develop. It is also located close to another large area of development, such as settlement Z, so settlement Y could be a commuter area. While settlement Z has limited space to expand because of its location in a meander loop, settlement Y does not have restrictions and can expand more easily.

121. Land use and settlement shapes

Use evidence from the map to support your points, which might include: there are only isolated areas of woodland; there are woods on the south bank of the river to the west of Sellack and next to the court at Baysham; there is a small plantation of mixed woodland at 565297; there is another small plantation around the road junction at Pennoxstone.

122. Human activity and OS maps

Your answers could include two of the following.

Facility	Symbol
Information centre	*i*
School	Sch
Church	✝
Camp site	△
Public house	PH

123. Map symbols and direction

1. Public telephone
2. North-west

124. Grid references and distances

1. 2 km (to the nearest whole number)
2. Mixed woodland
3. 112911

125. Cross sections and relief

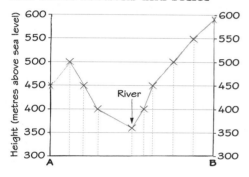

126. Graphical skills 1

Suggestions: (a) line graph; (b) scattergraph; (c) pie chart

127. Graphical skills 2

The percentage of people unemployed has increased significantly across the UK from 1979 to 1983. In particular, in the south-east the number of people unemployed has increased from 200 000 to 736 000, while in Scotland the number of people unemployed has increased from 100 000 to 400 000. East Anglia is the only area which did not experience an increase in the number of people unemployed.

128. Graphical skills 3

One advantage of using choropleth maps is the ability to plot a wide range of data to show geographical variations.

129. Numerical and statistical skills 1

Population increase is worked out by:
- finding the increase: new number − original number
  so 21 million − 8 million = 13 million
- dividing the increase by the original number and × 100
  so 13 million ÷ 8 million = 1.625 × 100 = 162.5%

130. Numerical and statistical skills 2

The interquartile range is the difference between the upper quartile and the lower quartile.
The lower quartile is worked out on the page as being 5 and the upper quartile as 11.
11 − 5 = 6

Published by Pearson Education Limited, 80 Strand, London, WC2R 0RL.

www.pearsonschoolsandfecolleges.co.uk

Copies of official specifications for all Pearson qualifications may be found on the website: qualifications.pearson.com

Text and illustrations © Pearson Education Limited 2016
Typeset and illustrations by Kamae Design, Oxford
Produced by Cambridge Publishing Management Ltd
Cover illustration by Miriam Sturdee

The right of Michael Chiles to be identified as author of this work has been asserted by him in accordance with the Copyright, Designs and Patents Act 1988.

First published 2016

19
10 9 8 7 6 5

British Library Cataloguing in Publication Data
A catalogue record for this book is available from the British Library

ISBN 978 1 292 13377 5

Acknowledgements
Content is included from Rob Bircher, David Flint, Anne-Marie Grant and Kirsty Taylor.

The author and publisher would like to thank the following individuals and organisations for permission to reproduce photographs:

(Key: b-bottom; c-centre; l-left; r-right; t-top)

Alamy Images: AidanStock 4, Andy Myatt 47l, Angela Hampton Picture Library 99r, 102r, Barry Lewis 66r, blickwinkel 19, Catherine Hoggins 12, Citizen of the Planet 23, Construction Photography 58r, Craig Holmes Premium 62, David Bagnall 58l, David Gowans 119, Dean Hoskins 52cr, Edward Moss 58cr, Filipe Frazao 47r, FLPA 102l, Friedrich Stark 71tc, Green Stock Media 48br, Ian Dagnall Commercial Collection 104, imageBROKER 1, 86, Jeff Morgan 15 115l, Jon Sparks 26l, Karina Tkach 64cr, Malcolm Park English coastline 10l, Matthew Postlethwaite 113l, MS Bretherton 53t, nobleIMAGES 71cl, Novarc Images 93, paul weston 63, Richard Wayman 115t, Rob Hawkins 99l, robertharding 71cr, RooM the Agency Mobile 64bl, Tony Watson 113r, Travelmania 18cl; **Fotolia.com:** Bikeworldtravel 112, Cloudia Spinner 118tr, harvepino 117, miket 118tl, Patryk Kosmider 10r, smartin69 18cr; **Getty Images:** Frank Bienewald 88r, Geography Photos 107, Ian Forsyth 87, Independent Picture Service 66l, Photofusion 21, Tim Graham 53br; **NASA:** NASA Earth Observatory 43; **Pearson Education Ltd:** Tudor Photography 52r; **PhotoDisc:** 118cl; **Rex Shutterstock:** David Bagnall 58cl; **Shutterstock.com:** bikeriderlondon 69, Bobkeenan Photography 27, Hugh Lansdown 46, Jiri Hera 52l, JP Chretien 52cl, Michael Hilton 26c, Paul Nash 3, PRILL 88l, pzAxe 51, Rich Carey 48t, Stephan Guarch 118cr, Stephen Finn 110, Takamex 67, Wollertz 118br

All other images © Pearson Education

We are grateful to the following for permission to reproduce copyright material:

Maps
Maps on page 3, page 4, page 9, page 10, page 18, page 20, page 26, page 30, page 98, page 101, page 117, page 119, page 120, page 121, page 122, page 123, page 124 from Ordnance Survey, © Crown copyright and database rights (2016) OS (100030901);

Maps International is a trading name of Lovell Johns Ltd; maps created by Lovell Johns Limited. Based upon Ordnance Survey digital map data © Crown Copyright 2013 Licence Number 43368U. All rights reserved. Map on page 70 adapted from http://data.worldbank.org/indicator/NY.GDP.PCAP.CD?view=map&year=2014, Source: World Bank national accounts data, and OECD National Accounts data files., © 2016 The World Bank Group, All Rights Reserved; Map on page 75 adapted from http://statisticstimes.com/economy/gdp-capita-of-indian-states.php; Map on page 83 from http://www.eia.gov/todayinenergy/detail.cfm?id=4210, U.S. Energy Information Administration, International Energy Statistics, 2011; Map on page 94 adapted from http://www.wri.org/sites/default/files/water_stress_by_country_0.png, Source: WRI Aqueduct, Gassert et al. 2013; Map on page 128 from Indices of Multiple Deprivation explorer: http://dclgapps.communities.gov.uk/imd/idmap.html © 2016 HERE, © 2016 Intermap, © 2016 Microsoft Corporation, Department For Communities and Local Government Contains public sector information licensed under the Open Government Licence v3.0.

Graphs
Graph on page 17 adapted from http://www.orkneyweather.co.uk/; Graph on page 76 adapted from World Bank data, OECD data, MEA data, © 2016 The World Bank Group, All Rights Reserved; Graph on page 90 adapted from http://www.wrsc.org/attach_image/global-water-consumption-1900-2025; Graph on page 110 adapted from http://www.marketoracle.co.uk/, (c) 2005-2016 MarketOracle.co.uk; Graph on page 111 adapted from *The Office for National Statistics, Long Term International Migration by Citizenship Data*, Office for National Statistics licensed under the Open Government Licence v.3.0.

Screenshot
Screenshot on page 43 from http://earthobservatory.nasa.gov/IOTD/view.php?id=40997, NASA Earth Observatory image by Jesse Allen and Robert Simmon using EO-1 ALI data courtesy of the NASA EO-1 team

Case Study
Case Study on page 58, page 59, page 60, page 61 adapted from http://www.birmingham.gov.uk/, Birmingham City Council, © Crown copyright. Contains public sector information licensed under the Open Government Licence (OGL) v3.0. http://www.nationalarchives.gov.uk/doc/open-government

Notes from the publisher

1. In order to ensure that this resource offers high-quality support for the associated Pearson qualification, it has been through a review process by the awarding body. This process confirms that this resource fully covers the teaching and learning content of the specification or part of a specification at which it is aimed. It also confirms that it demonstrates an appropriate balance between the development of subject skills, knowledge and understanding, in addition to preparation for assessment.

Endorsement does not cover any guidance on assessment activities or processes (e.g. practice questions or advice on how to answer assessment questions), included in the resource nor does it prescribe any particular approach to the teaching or delivery of a related course.

While the publishers have made every attempt to ensure that advice on the qualification and its assessment is accurate, the official specification and associated assessment guidance materials are the only authoritative source of information and should always be referred to for definitive guidance.

Pearson examiners have not contributed to any sections in this resource relevant to examination papers for which they have responsibility.

Examiners will not use endorsed resources as a source of material for any assessment set by Pearson.

Endorsement of a resource does not mean that the resource is required to achieve this Pearson qualification, nor does it mean that it is the only suitable material available to support the qualification, and any resource lists produced by the awarding body shall include this and other appropriate resources.

2. Pearson has robust editorial processes, including answer and fact checks, to ensure the accuracy of the content in this publication, and every effort is made to ensure this publication is free of errors. We are, however, only human, and occasionally errors do occur. Pearson is not liable for any misunderstandings that arise as a result of errors in this publication, but it is our priority to ensure that the content is accurate. If you spot an error, please do contact us at resourcescorrections@pearson.com so we can make sure it is corrected.